Hamlyn nature guides

Minerals

HAMLYN NATURE GUIDES
MINERALS

ANDREW CLARK

HAMLYN

Acknowledgements

Ardea Photographics – P. J. Green 20L, 21L; F. B. Atkins – 88L; R. Böck – 112L; Herve Chaumenton – 41L, 47R, 51L, 67L, 88R, 90L, 99L, 103L, 110R, 112R, 114R, 116L, 117L, 123R, 124L; A. W. Curtis – 27L, 32R, 56R, 56L, 72R, 81R, 98R; Adrian Davies – 109L; Hamlyn Group Picture Library – 87L, 111R, 115L; Imitor Ltd.– 16L, 109R, 111L; Jacana – 19L, 59L, 93L, 110L, 113R; Breck P. Kent – 16R, 17L, 18L, 20R, 21R, 23L, 23R, 24L, 26R, 28L, 28R, 29L, 29R, 32L, 36R, 37L, 38L, 38R, 39L, 41R, 45L, 48R, 55L, 55R, 57L, 57R, 58L, 58R, 60R, 61R, 62R, 64R, 66L, 66R, 72L, 73R, 75L, 75R, 76L, 76R, 77L, 77R, 79L, 81L, 82R, 84R, 86L, 89R, 91L, 92R, 94L, 97L, 98L, 100L, 104R, 105L, 113L, 119L, 119R, 121R, 122R, 125L; I. Patterson – 18R, 19R, 22L, 24R, 25L, 25R, 26R, 27R, 30L, 31L, 31R, 33L, 33R, 34L, 35L, 36L, 37R, 39R, 40L, 40R, 42L, 42R, 43L, 44L, 44R, 45R, 46L, 46R, 47L, 48L, 49L, 49R, 50L, 50R, 51R, 52L, 53L, 53R, 54L, 56R, 59R, 60L, 62L, 63L, 63R, 64L, 65L, 65R, 67R, 68L, 69R, 70L, 70R, 71L, 71R, 73L, 74L, 74R, 75R, 78L, 78R, 80R, 82L, 84L, 85L, 85R, 86R, 87R, 89L, 90R, 91R, 92L, 93R, 94R, 95R, 96L, 96R, 97R, 99R, 99R, 100R, 100R, 101L, 101R, 102L, 102R, 103R, 106R, 107L, 107R, 108L, 108R, 115R, 116R, 117R, 118R, 120L, 120R, 122L, 124R, 125R; J. C. Revy – 43R, 61L, 69L, 80L, 105R, 106L, 123L; RIDA Photo Library – David Baylis – 22R; R. Symes – 54R; Z.E.F.A. – W. F. Davidson – 52R.

The following photographs are reproduced by courtesy of the Smithsonian Institution, Washington D.C.: 18L, 23L, 28L, 29R, 32L, 48R, 57L, 58L, 58R, 72L, 75L, 76L, 76R, 77L, 77R, 79L, 91L, 92R, 94L, 100L.

The following photographs are N.E.R.C. copyright and are reproduced by permission of the Director, Institute of Geological Sciences, London: 17R, 30L, 34R, 35R, 68R, 79R, 83L, 83R, 104L, 114L, 118L, 121L.

The photographs taken by I. Patterson are reproduced from the private collection of Dr. R. J. King, Leicester.

Title spread photograph: Arnold Fisher/Science Photo Library
Front cover: adamite
Back cover: limonite
Title spread: rosasite

Line drawings by Valerie Jones
First published 1979
This soft cover edition published 1989 by
The Hamlyn Publishing Group Ltd.,
now a division of The Octopus Publishing Group,
Michelin House, 81 Fulham Road,
London SW3 6RB

Phototypeset by Photocomp Ltd

Produced by Mandarin Offset
Printed and bound in Hong Kong

Contents

Introduction
Chemistry and structure

Minerals are the naturally occurring chemical compounds from which all rocks are formed. Their compositions can usually be expressed by formulae indicating the elements present (Table I) and the proportions in which they are combined. A chemical compound is normally regarded as being made up of two parts, a positively charged or cationic part and a negatively charged or anionic part. To be stable the resulting compound must be electrically neutral with the anionic and cationic charges balancing. The cationic part is normally composed of metallic elements, while the anionic part can be formed of either a non-metallic ion such as oxygen or a combination of several elements forming an anionic group, such as a carbonate (CO_3), sulphate (SO_4), or silicate (SiO_4, etc.).

The forces binding together the various atoms in a mineral are essentially electrical in nature. Known as bonds, they play a large part in determining a mineral's chemical and physical properties. The most important bonds are: 1) the metallic bond, common in the native metals and some sulphides; 2) the covalent bond, of most importance in organic compounds but also found in some minerals, e.g. diamond (Fig. 1); 3) the ionic bond, the most important in mineralogy as over 90% of the known mineral species can be considered as ionic compounds.

In the Earth's crust eight elements (oxygen, silicon, aluminium, iron, calcium, sodium, potassium, magnesium) form the bulk of the rock-forming silicate minerals and constitute nearly 99% of its mass.

Table I Chemical elements commonly found in minerals, arranged in order of increasing atomic weight

element	symbol	element	symbol	element	symbol
hydrogen	H	calcium	Ca	cadmium	Cd
lithium	Li	titanium	Ti	tin	Sn
beryllium	Be	vanadium	V	antimony	Sb
boron	B	chromium	Cr	barium	Ba
carbon	C	manganese	Mn	lanthanum	La
nitrogen	N	iron	Fe	cerium	Ce
oxygen	O	cobalt	Co	tantalum	Ta
fluorine	F	nickel	Ni	tungsten	W
sodium	Na	copper	Cu	platinum	Pt
magnesium	Mg	zinc	Zn	gold	Au
aluminium	Al	arsenic	As	mercury	Hg
silicon	Si	strontium	Sr	lead	Pb
phosphorus	P	yttrium	Y	bismuth	Bi
sulphur	S	zirconium	Zr	thorium	Th
chlorine	Cl	molybdenum	Mo	uranium	U
potassium	K	silver	Ag		

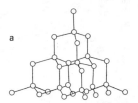
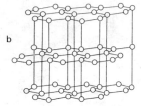

Fig. 1 *The structure of diamond (a) and graphite (b). Both minerals are covalent compounds and composed of pure carbon. Diamond crystallizes in the cubic system but graphite is hexagonal and the planes of structural weakness in graphite can be clearly seen. This results in graphite being one of the softest minerals whereas diamond is the hardest.*

Crystals

Mineralogy is a science largely concerned with the crystalline state. A crystal is a body bounded by smooth plane surfaces (faces) that are the external expression of an orderly internal atomic arrangement. Minerals, when occurring under conditions favourable to crystal growth, will form well developed crystals. However, if the growing crystals interfere with each other they are often poorly formed or distorted. The mineral is still described as crystalline, for no matter how imperfectly formed, it has the same ordered atomic structure and definite chemical composition. Even before the development of the advanced scientific techniques we know today, it was realized that the arrangement of the faces on a crystallized mineral and the angles between these faces were characteristic for that given mineral species. This means that, no matter how poorly formed the crystal is, or of what habit, the angle between the same two faces (if developed) in all crystals of the same mineral species is constant (Fig. 2). This regularity of faces and angles led to the understanding that crystals were symmetrical bodies and could be classified according to that symmetry.

Fig. 2 *The law of constancy of interfacial angles. Crystals of the same mineral may assume different shapes due to the unequal development of the faces, yet the angles between similar faces remain constant.*

Symmetry

Ideas related to symmetry are therefore important in describing the shapes of crystals and their internal atomic arrangement. To subdivide crystals into symmetry groups three elements of symmetry are used. 1) *Planes of symmetry* Crystals can be symmetrical about a plane; that is, if a crystal is cut in half along that plane, one half will be the mirror image of the other. 2) *Axis of symmetry* Crystals can be symmetrical about an imaginary line or axis passing through their centre. For instance, a cube has a four-fold symmetry axis

7

passing at right angles through the centre of any of its faces (Fig. 3). If rotated it appears the same four times in each complete rotation. A rectangular block has only a two-fold axis of symmetry passing at right angles through the centre of any face, and on rotation the same faces occur only twice in a revolution. 3) *Centre of symmetry* Crystals sometimes have a centre of symmetry when a face on the crystal has a corresponding parallel face on the other side of the crystal. On the basis of these symmetry elements, crystallographers assign crystals to six crystal classes. A seventh class (trigonal) is recognized by most mineralogists (Table II). This has the same set of reference axes as the hexagonal system but has a vertical three-fold axis of symmetry.

Table II Crystal axes and symmetry in the seven crystal classes

System	Axes	Symmetry
Cubic	Three equal axes mutually perpendicular	Four three-fold axes
Tetragonal	Three axes at right-angles, two of equal length	One four-fold axis
Hexagonal	Three equal axes in a horizontal plane and a fourth of different length perpendicular to this plane	One six-fold axis
Trigonal	As for hexagonal	One three-fold axis
Monoclinic	Three axes of unequal length, two of which are not at right-angles	One two-fold axis
Triclinic	Three unequal axes, none at right-angles	A centre of symmetry *or* no symmetry

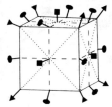

Fig. 3 *Planes of symmetry (shown as dotted and broken lines) and axes of symmetry in a cube.*
● *represents a two-fold axis,* ▲ *a three-fold axis, and* ■ *a four-fold axis.*

Crystal form

All the crystal faces of a mineral having a similar appearance and a like position with respect to the elements of symmetry for that particular mineral are said to have the same form. A crystal form therefore consists of all those faces required by the symmetry of the crystal. Crystals of the same mineral often show a range of different shapes according to which crystal forms or combinations of forms are developed (Fig. 4). Some forms such as the cube and octahedron totally enclose space and can form crystals by themselves; these are called *closed forms* (Fig. 5). Some forms, however, are termed *open forms*, that is, they do not enclose a volume of space and so can only form solid crystals if they occur in combination with other forms. Prisms, for instance, are an open form and in prismatic crystals the ends are terminated by other faces (forms), e.g. pyramids. The cubic system having the highest symmetry has fifteen forms in all, some of which are rarely observed. The common forms are the tetrahedron (4-faced), the cube (6-faced), the octahedron (8-faced), the dodecahedron (12-faced) and the icositetrahedron (24-faced). Many combinations of these can occur.

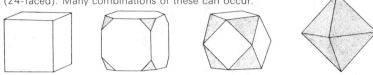

Fig. 4 *Combinations of the cubic and octahedral forms.*

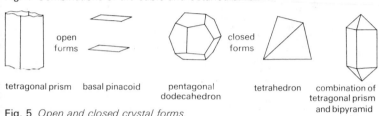

tetragonal prism   basal pinacoid   pentagonal dodecahedron   tetrahedron   combination of tetragonal prism and bipyramid

open forms   closed forms

Fig. 5 *Open and closed crystal forms.*

Crystal habit

Another important aspect in the study of crystals is the overall shape of the crystal known as its habit. This feature can be so characteristic of a particular mineral that often no other is needed to establish its identity (Fig. 6). Most minerals occur as aggregates of crystals, large single crystals being comparatively rare. Descriptive terms are applied to the form of the aggregates:

Botryoidal	resembling a bunch of grapes
Reniform	kidney-shaped
Globular	more or less spherical
Fibrous	consisting of long thin crystals
Foliated or lamellar	consisting of sheets that easily split apart
Radiating	spreading outward from a single point
Dendritic	resembling a fern.

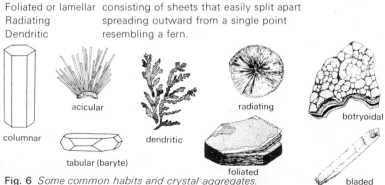

columnar   acicular   dendritic   radiating   botryoidal

tabular (baryte)   foliated   bladed

Fig. 6 *Some common habits and crystal aggregates.*

Twinning

Twinned crystals are those having the appearance of two or more individual crystals (in contact or interpenetration), that are identical and mirror images of one another. The individual parts of the twin must be related by a definite crystallographic law. Such crystals are usually described as either simple or repeated, contact or penetration twins. They may be interpenetrant as in staurolite; or repeatedly twinned (polysynthetic), if the successive twinned composition surfaces are parallel, as in plagioclase feldspars; or cyclic, if the composition surfaces are not parallel, often forming geniculate twins as in rutile.

Optical properties

Colour

The colour shown by a mineral is due to the selective absorption of certain wavelengths of white light by the mineral. The resulting colour is virtually white light minus the absorbed wavelengths. The causes of the colour in minerals are varied and complex and identification of specimens by this alone needs care since single species can show a wide range of colour. Sometimes colour is directly related to chemical composition, as in the typical blues and greens of most secondary copper minerals. However, it may be due to differences in the crystal structure or bonding (graphite and diamond) or to crystal growth defects, or also sometimes to contained impurities and inclusions.

Transparency

A very obvious property of a mineral specimen is its tendency to be either transparent, translucent or opaque. This property is a measure of the amount of light absorbed by the mineral, this being dependent upon the internal structure and chemical bonding of the mineral.

Lustre

The nature of a mineral's surface is the controlling factor in the amount of light reflected. Different surfaces produce different intensities of lustre and various terms are applied to describe these grades of lustre. *Metallic lustre*. This is shown by those minerals which are similar to metals; they absorb light strongly and are therefore opaque even in the thinnest fragments. *Non-metallic lustre*. There are various types of non-metallic lustre:

Vitreous	having a lustre characteristic of broken glass
Resinous	similar to that of resin
Adamantine	similar to that of diamond
Pearly	a lustre resulting from the reflection of light from parallel surfaces within the crystal
Silky	the lustre produced by the presence of fine parallel fibres as in some varieties of gypsum
Earthy	lack of lustre due to surfaces that scatter the light.

Minerals that have little or no lustre at all are described as dull.

Streak

The colour of the fine powder of a mineral is known as its streak. When a specimen is drawn across a piece of unglazed porcelain, known as a streak plate, a line of colour (streak) may result. This test is frequently used in mineral identification especially in the field because, although the colour of a mineral may vary greatly, the colour of the streak is usually constant.

Physical properties

Specific gravity (S.G.)

This is defined as the ratio of the weight of a given volume of mineral to the weight of an equal volume of water. It is a property which is dependent largely on the chemical nature of the atoms in the mineral and on the atomic packing in the structure. Instances occur of minerals of the same chemical composition having different S.G.'s due to denser atomic packing. Also minerals with a similar structure may have different S.G.'s due to the presence of heavier atoms in the structure. Minerals often show a range of S.G.'s due to chemical substitution. For example, the S.G. of the tetrahedrite series varies between 4·6 and 5·1 as a result of the replacement of arsenic by antimony in the structure.

Hardness

This is the ability of a metal to resist scratching or abrasion by other minerals or materials. It is related to the internal atomic structure and to the strength of the chemical bonding of the mineral. Mineralogists use the scale of hardness devised by F. Mohs in which ten minerals are arranged in an order of increasing hardness so that each will scratch those lower in the scale.

1 Talc (softest)   2 Gypsum   3 Calcite   4 Fluorite   5 Apatite   6 Ortho-clase   7 Quartz   8 Topaz   9 Corundum   10 Diamond (hardest)

An unknown mineral is tested by deciding whether or not minerals of the Mohs' scale scratch the specimen. A hand lens is often necessary to be positive of the result. For field tests it is useful to know that the fingernail has a hardness of about $2\frac{1}{2}$; a steel pocket-knife blade about $5\frac{1}{2}$; and minerals of 6 and over will scratch glass. Quantitative hardnesses of materials are determined from the size of an indentation produced in the material by a controlled load, but these can still be related to the Mohs' scale.

Cleavage

Many minerals show cleavage, that is, the property of crystals to break readily in certain directions along plane surfaces. Cleavage surfaces are always parallel to crystal faces or possible crystal faces. This property is dependent upon the atomic structure, and in this case, the bond strength between different atoms, or planes of atoms, in the structure. For instance, in the mica group of minerals, chemical bonds between the silicon-oxygen layers are weak and the micas therefore cleave or split easily into thin sheets. The degree of perfection of cleavage varies between minerals so that less than *perfect* cleavages are described as *good, poor,* or *indistinct*. Where the mineral species has the property of cleavage, it usually shows in all specimens of that mineral, but parting is a property which may appear in some specimens of a mineral but not in all. Parting planes arise where stress develops planes of structural weakness along which crystals may be broken, for instance, twin crystals often part along the twin composition plane. Occasionally when a mineral specimen is broken it does not cleave or part along any definite plane, but simply fractures to leave an irregular surface. The nature of this irregular surface may be characteristic of the mineral and is known as the *fracture.* Different fractures are described as:

Conchoidal	typical of quartz, flint and sometimes glass, usually smooth curved surfaces like the interior of a shell (Fig. 7).
Splintery	breaks into splinters
Hackly	breaks with a jagged, irregular surface with sharp edges
Uneven or irregular	rough surfaces.

Fig. 7 *Conchoidal fracture, the commonest type of fracture surface found in minerals.*

Tenacity
This is a property closely linked with the hardness of a mineral but defined as its toughness. A mineral is classed as *sectile* when it can be cut with the blade of a knife without powdering. If the specimen powders or breaks easily, it is decribed as *brittle*. The term *malleable* is used if a section of the specimen can be hammered flat without powdering and is typical of the native metals. If thin fragments of the material can be bent without breaking, and remain bent, they are known as *flexible*, whereas *ductile* means that the material can be drawn into a wire.

Other properties

Magnetism. Minerals that are attracted to a magnet are said to be magnetic. The minerals magnetite and pyrrhotine are the most common of the magnetic minerals. Other minerals showing varied magnetic properties are described in the minerals classification section.

Fluorescence. Some minerals become luminescent during exposure to ultra-violet light. The colour of the luminescence is usually characteristic of the species present. However, not all specimens of the same species show fluorescence as this may be due to fluorescence caused by impurities in the specimen.

Radioactivity. A number of species containing radioactive elements emit radioactivity. This can be tested with a Geiger counter. Most specimens of primary and secondary uranium and thorium minerals will exhibit this property.

There are many varied chemical tests which can be applied to fragments of mineral specimens to help in identification, usually by determining the elements present in the mineral, but you should have access to good laboratory facilities before performing these tests. However, the reaction of dilute or concentrated acids on certain minerals is characteristic; for example, the action of hydrochloric acid on carbonates producing effervescence, is typical. Also certain minerals when volatilized in a flame, will give a characteristic colour to a flame if certain elements are present; e.g. barium colours a flame apple-green. The test is best performed using the powdered mineral on a piece of platinum wire.

Rocks and mineral deposits

All rocks are composed of mineral grains and the major minerals present in a rock serve as a basis of petrological classification. In many coarse-grained rocks, such as granites, individual mineral grains can be clearly seen with the naked eye, whereas in basalts and other fine-grained rocks, microscopic examination is required.

Igneous rocks

Igneous rocks are formed by the solidification of molten rock material known as *magma*. Most magma is thought to originate within the Earth from a layer of dense rock called the *mantle* lying beneath the less dense *crust*. The crust is about 35 km thick under the continents but as little as 7 km under the oceans. Magma rising through the crust towards the Earth's surface crystallizes as *igneous intrusions*, such rocks usually being of a medium- to coarse-grain size. Magma reaching the surface is extruded as *lava* which cools rapidly resulting in a fine-grained appearance. The most common rock formed as a lava is the dark and dense rock known as *basalt*, whereas the most common intrusive rock is *granite*. The classification of igneous rocks is based on an assessment of the grain size and mineralogical composition — the important minerals used in this classification are quartz, the feldspars, feldspathoids, pyroxenes, amphiboles, micas, and olivines.

Metamorphic rocks

Metamorphism is the process by which pre-existing sedimentary and igneous rocks are mineralogically and texturally altered by heat and pressure within the Earth. As these processes take place generally at temperatures below the melting point of the rock, metamorphic minerals grow in a solid environment. Typical of these minerals are garnet, staurolite and kyanite. *Contact metamorphic rocks* are produced by high temperatures but low pressures, and are to be found near the contact with an igneous intrusion (metamorphic aureole — Fig. 8). Metamorphism on a larger scale, involving mountain building and other tectonic activities, results in *regionally metamorphosed rocks*. Their formation takes place at high temperatures and high pressures, kyanite and sillimanite being typical minerals formed under these conditions. Rocks formed under high pressure usually show a marked foliated texture, as in the common metamorphic rocks known as *schists* and *gneisses*. *Slates* have a similar appearance but can in addition be split into sheets. *Hornfels* is a fine-grained, even-textured rock resulting from thermal metamorphism. Most changes in metamorphic rocks take place in the solid state, but often movement of fluids through a rock occurs and this may give rise to chemical reactions, or it may add or remove material from the rock. This process is known as *metasomatism* and it occurs particularly around contact metamorphic deposits.

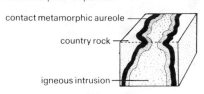

contact metamorphic aureole

country rock

igneous intrusion

Fig. 8 *The contact metamorphic aureole surrounding an igneous intrusion.*

Sedimentary rocks

This important group of rocks is formed by surface processes on the Earth and the minerals involved are therefore products of low temperatures and pressures.

Sediments originating *mechanically* are composed of solid particles of weathered or abraded rock transported by water, wind or ice, forming sedimentary deposits in lakes, river mouths or seas. The particles subsequently become compacted into rocks of which typical types are conglomerates (coarse-grained), sandstones (medium-grained) or shales (fine-grained).

A *chemical* mode of origin applies to those sediments which precipitate or crystallize from solutions. *Evaporites* are a very important group under this heading forming when water evaporates from an enclosed body of sea-water or when the solution becomes saturated with salts. Rock salts, flints, and some limestones owe their origins to these and related processes.

Sediments formed *organically* result from the accumulation of organic material, such as bones or plant material and their subsequent consolidation into rocks. Oolitic limestone, chalk and coal are formed in this way.

Ore deposits

Of great importance to the demands of technology and the world economy are the metalliferous and non-metalliferous mineral deposits.

A number of heavy and relatively insoluble minerals such as gold, cassiterite and ilmenite readily form 'placer' or alluvial deposits after erosion and transportation from their original sites.

During the cooling and consolidation of some magmas, concentrations of certain minerals may form segregation deposits due to the gravity settling of the component crystals. The chromite-rich layers of the Bushveld complex in South Africa are an example.

As magma cools and crystallizes the remaining solution becomes more acidic and enriched with metallic components and other volatile and gaseous elements. These fluids may react with the pre-existing country rocks to form *contact metasomatic deposits*. For instance, residual liquids rich in boron and other volatiles lead to the extensive tourmalinization of many shales, slates or granites. During the final stages of magma consolidation highly siliceous molten liquids may penetrate into the intrusive rocks and country rocks to form *pegmatite* veins. Comparatively rare minerals may form in large crystals in these veins: lithium minerals, phosphates, beryl and the niobates and tantalates are typical pegmatitic species.

The economically important sulphide ores are mainly deposited in the later stages of magma consolidation at temperatures between 50°C and 500°C. in what are known as *hydrothermal deposits*. These result from the crystallization of residual solutions in fractures and fissures in the surrounding rocks. These solutions form veins or lodes with both the ore and gangue minerals (minerals with no commercial value associated with the ore), often showing characteristic banding parallel to the wall of the vein. Often these fissures are not completely filled and 'cavities' or 'vugs' are formed, often being lined with well-developed crystals (Fig. 9). These vugs are eagerly sought after by mineral collectors for their mineral content.

Fig. 9 *A hydrothermal vein and a mineral-bearing vug.*

Replacement deposits are found when mineralizing solutions, instead of filling fractures, dissolve material and replace the rock. This is liable to occur in soluble rocks like limestones.

Fig. 10 *Weathering and secondary enrichment of a hydrothermal sulphide vein.*

- gossan or ironhat
- zone of leaching
- zone of oxide enrichment
- water table — zone of secondary sulphide enrichment
- unaltered ore

Secondary enrichment involves the alteration of hydrothermal deposits by weathering processes (Fig. 10). Water descending through a hydrothermal vein from the Earth's surface takes the ore minerals into solution leaving a cavernous leached rock rich in silica and iron oxides ('gossan' or 'ironhat'). The metals become concentrated in the oxidizing solutions and will be deposited as a concentrated layer of oxide minerals, Below the water table an area of oxygen deficiency occurs and metals remaining in solution are redeposited as secondary sulphides rather than sulphates and carbonates. Below this level the vein reverts to its original unaltered state. The zone of secondary enrichment therefore often contains the redeposited metals from several hundred metres of leached rock.

The minerals described in this book are arranged in a conventional chemical sequence. The descriptions are made under four main headings habit, colour, occurrence and distinguishing properties; the last being those properties of the mineral species which are most important in identification.

Native elements

Gold

Au Cubic **Habit** Crystals are rare (cubic, octahedral and dodecahedral); usually dendritic growths, occasionally as rounded masses. Often as alluvial grains. Twinning is common on octahedral planes. **Colour** Golden-yellow, lighter yellow with increasing silver content; opaque. Golden-yellow streak. Metallic lustre. **Occurrence** Small amounts in hydrothermal veins, associated commonly with quartz and pyrite. Due to resistance to chemical alteration and density, the grains become concentrated into alluvial deposits, and may be consolidated into conglomerates. **Distinguishing properties** Colour; S.G. 19·3 pure; hardness $2\frac{1}{2}$–3; insoluble in single acids; hackly fracture; malleable and ductile. Pyrite (fool's gold) and chalcopyrite are readily distinguished from gold by their greater hardness and brittle nature.

Silver

Ag Cubic **Habit** Crystals are rar sometimes cubic, octahedral or dode cahedral, usually massive, scaly wiry aggregates. Twinning is commc on octahedral planes. **Colour** Silve white tarnishing rapidly to grey black; opaque. Metallic lustre. Silve white streak. **Occurrence** Usuall in hydrothermal veins, or in the oxidize zone of silver-bearing ore deposit Sometimes found in conglomerate or placer deposits. **Distinguishin properties** Colour, black tarnish; S.C 10·5 (for the pure metal), silver ofte contains considerable gold or mercur (mercury-rich varieties are known a amalgam); hardness $2\frac{1}{2}$–3; hackl fracture; malleable and ductile. Solubl in nitric acid.

Copper

Cu Cubic **Habit** Crystals usually cubic or dodecahedral, commonly occurring as dendritic forms, or wire-like crystal growths. Twinning is common on octahedral planes. **Colour** Bright copper-red on fresh surfaces tarnishing to a dull brown colour and often superficially coated with black or green crusts; opaque. Metallic-copper red streak. Metallic lustre. **Occurrence** Commonly found in the oxidized zones of copper deposits associated with cuprite, malachite and azurite. Also often associated with basic extrusive igneous rocks where copper has formed by the reaction of copper-bearing solutions with iron minerals. **Distinguishing properties** Habit; colour and tarnish; S.G. 8·9; hardness $2\frac{1}{2}$–3; hackly fracture; malleable and ductile. Soluble in nitric acid.

Platinum

Pt Cubic **Habit** Found as rare cubic crystals, usually in grains, scales or nuggets. **Colour** Steel-grey to silver-white; opaque. Metallic lustre. White to steel-grey streak. **Occurrence** In basic and ultrabasic igneous rocks, associated with olivine, pyroxene, chromite and magnetite, where it may form rich magmatic segregations. Also found as grains or nuggets in river gravels derived from areas of ultrabasic rocks. **Distinguishing properties** Colour; S.G. 14–19 (21·5 for pure metal), native platinum always contains iron, often copper and other platinum-group metals; hardness 4–$4\frac{1}{2}$; hackly fracture; malleable. Insoluble in all acids apart from hot aqua regia.

Iron and Nickel-iron

Fe and Fe-Ni Cubic **Habit** Native iron occurs very rarely as a terrestrial mineral in the form of grains and sometimes larger masses. In meteorites nickel-iron occurs intergrown as kamacite (Fe,Ni with 4–7% Ni) with taenite (Fe,Ni with 30–60% Ni) lamellar masses. **Colour** Steel-grey to black; opaque. Metallic lustre. Iron-grey streak. **Occurrence** Terrestrial native iron occurs rarely where volcanic rocks cut coal seams. The most important occurrence is on Disko Island in west Greenland. **Distinguishing properties** Strongly magnetic; S.G. 7·3–8·2; hardness 4–5; poor cubic cleavage; hackly fracture; malleable.

Arsenic

As Hexagonal (Trigonal) **Habit** Crystals are very rare, usually massive occurring as granular or botryoidal masses. **Colour** Light grey on fresh surfaces, rapidly tarnishing to dark grey; opaque. Metallic lustre. Light grey streak. **Occurrence** As a constituent of some hydrothermal veins commonly associated with silver, cobalt and nickel minerals. **Distinguishing properties** Habit; characteristic garlic odour when heated. Can easily be confused with native antimony but when heated on a charcoal block arsenic volatilizes whereas antimony melts to a metallic globule. S.G. 5·6–5·8; hardness $3\frac{1}{2}$; perfect basal cleavage; uneven granular fracture.

Antimony

b Hexagonal (Trigonal) **Habit** rystals are rare, usually massive, ccurring as lamellar, botryoidal or niform (kidney-shaped) masses. winning is common. **Colour** Light rey; opaque. Metallic lustre. Grey treak. **Occurrence** In hydrothermal eins, associated with silver minerals, ften associated with stibnite, also phalerite, pyrite and galena. **Distinguishing properties** Habit; distinguished from arsenic by the lack of haracteristic odour on heating. S.G. ·6–6·7; hardness 3–3½; perfect basal leavage; uneven fracture.

Bismuth

Bi Hexagonal (Trigonal) **Habit** Rare as crystals, usually granular masses or in reticulated or arborescent forms. Twinning is frequent, often polysynthetic. **Colour** Silver-white, with a reddish hue which darkens with exposure. Often an irridescent tarnish is developed; opaque. Metallic lustre. Silver-white, shiny streak. **Occurrence** In hydrothermal veins, associated with ores of cobalt, nickel, silver and tin. **Distinguishing properties** Distinguished from antimony by colour, melts readily at 270°C forming a product soluble in nitric acid. S.G. 9·7–9·8; hardness 2–2½; perfect basal cleavage; brittle when cold, malleable when heated.

Sulphur

S Orthorhombic **Habit** Crystals thick
tabular or bipyramidal, also as massive,
stalactitic or powdery aggregates.
Colour Bright yellow to yellowish
brown; transparent to translucent.
Resinous to greasy lustre. White streak.
Occurrence As a sublimation product
of volcanic gases, encrusting volcanic
vents or fumaroles; also deposited
from some thermal springs. Sulphur is
most commonly found in sedimentary
rocks associated with gypsum and
limestone; often occurs in the cap
rocks of salt domes in association
with anhydrite, gypsum and calcite.
Distinguishing properties Colour; S.G.
$2 \cdot 0 – 2 \cdot 1$; hardness $1\frac{1}{2} – 2\frac{1}{2}$; uneven to
conchoidal fracture; slightly sectile.
Low melting point ($113°C$); insoluble
in water and dilute hydrochloric acid
but soluble in carbon disulphide.

Diamond

C (pure carbon) Cubic **Habit** Com
monly occurs as octahedral crysta
also cubic, dodecahedral, tetrahedr
often with curved faces. Twinning
common on the octahedral plan
Colour Colourless, sometimes pa
yellow, blue, green, red or even blac
transparent to translucent. Gem quali
diamonds are clear. The colour ar
transparency of diamonds vary great
and have a considerable bearing c
their value. Bort is a grey to blac
variety, due to impurities and ir
clusions. Adamantine to greasy lustr
White streak. **Occurrence** Sporadical
distributed in ultrabasic rocks rich i
olivine and phlogopite (kimberlites
which form pipe-like intrusions. Als
in alluvial deposits, mainly as river an
beach gravels. **Distinguishing proper
ties** Habit and lustre; S.G. $3 \cdot 5$; extrem
hardness 10; perfect octahedral cleav
age; conchoidal fracture.

Graphite

(pure carbon) Hexagonal **Habit** flat tabular crystals, commonly massive, foliated, granular or earthy. Colour Black; opaque. Dull metallic or earthy lustre. Dark grey (pencil lead) streak, readily marks paper. **Occurrence** Formed by metamorphism of rocks having an appreciable carbon content. It can be found in crystalline limestones, schists, quartzites and metamorphosed coal-beds. Also found in some igneous rocks, veins and pegmatites. **Distinguishing properties** Colour; S.G. 2·1–2·3; hardness 1–2 (Extreme softness, greasy feel); perfect basal cleavage; sectile. Distinguished from molybdenite, a mineral of similar appearance, by its black streak, lower S.G. and colour.

Sulphides and sulphosalts

Argentite (Silver glance)

Ag_2S Cubic. Argentite is stable above 180°C, acanthite is the monoclinic modification which is stable below 180°C. **Habit** Crystals are commonly cubic or octahedral (paramorphs of acanthite after argentite). Frequently occurs as groups of crystals in parallel growth, also occurring as massive arborescent or filiform (wiry) aggregates. **Colour** Black; opaque. Metallic lustre. Black, shiny streak. **Occurrence** As a primary mineral in hydrothermal veins in association with pyrargyrite, proustite and native silver. Sometimes as microscopic inclusions in galena (argentiferous galena) **Distinguishing properties** Colour; S.G. 7·2–7·4; hardness 2–2½; poor cubic cleavage; subconchoidal fracture; sectile. Soluble in dilute nitric acid.

Chalcosine (Chalcocite, Copper Glance)

Cu_2S Orthorhombic **Habit** Crystals are short prismatic or thick tabular; usually massive. Twinning is common, giving pseudohexagonal forms. **Colour** Dark grey to black; opaque. Metallic lustre. Black streak. **Occurrence** Most commonly found in the secondary enriched zone of primary copper sulphides often associated with native copper or cuprite. Also in hydrothermal veins with chalcopyrite covelline and pyrite. **Distinguishing properties** Colour; association with other copper minerals. S.G. $5 \cdot 5 - 5 \cdot 8$; hardness $2\frac{1}{2} - 3$; prismatic indistinct cleavage; conchoidal fracture. Soluble in hot nitric acid. Often shows alteration to malachite or azurite.

Bornite (Peacock Ore, Erubescite)

Cu_5FeS_4 Cubic **Habit** Crystals a cubic or dodecahedral, the faces which are often rough or curve usually massive. Twinning is on th octahedral plane. **Colour** Copper-re to brown, tarnishing rapidly to characteristic purplish iridescenc opaque. Metallic lustre. Pale grey black streak. **Occurrence** A commc copper mineral found in hydrotherm veins, both as a primary constituer and as a product of secondary en richment. **Distinguishing propertie** Colour and iridescent tarnish (Peacoc Ore). S.G. 5.1; hardness 3; uneven t subconchoidal fracture. Alters t chalcosine, cuprite, malachite an azurite. Soluble in nitric acid.

Galena

PbS Cubic **Habit** Crystals are usually cubic, octahedral or cubo-octahedral, also massive or granular. Penetration and contact-twins on octahedral plane. **Colour** Lead-grey; opaque. Metallic lustre. Lead-grey streak. **Occurrence** Very widely distributed, the most important lead-ore. Found extensively in hydrothermal sulphide vein deposits associated with sphalerite, pyrite, chalcopyrite, tetrahedrite, bournonite and gangue minerals. In some high temperature veins or replacement deposits associated with garnet, diopside, rhodonite and biotite. Also as a replacement body in limestone and dolomite rocks. **Distinguishing properties** Colour and metallic lustre; S.G. 7·4–7·6; hardness $2\frac{1}{2}$; perfect cubic cleavage. Oxidizes readily to anglesite, cerussite, pyromorphite or mimetite.

Sphalerite (Blende)

ZnS Cubic **Habit** Crystals commonly tetrahedral or dodecahedral, often distorted with rough curved faces, also occurs massive, granular and sometimes fibrous. Twinning is common on octahedral plane. **Colour** Commonly yellow, brown to black with increasing iron content, sometimes red; transparent to translucent. Resinous to sub-metallic lustre. Brown to light yellow streak. **Occurrence** The most common zinc mineral. Occurs in hydrothermal ore veins, associated with other sulphides; as replacement ore-bodies in limestone, associated with pyrite, pyrrhotine and magnetite. **Distinguishing properties** Colour and lustre; S.G. 3·9–4·1; hardness $3\frac{1}{2}$–4; perfect dodecahedral cleavage; conchoidal fracture. Slowly soluble in hydrochloric acid with evolution of hydrogen sulphide. May alter to hemimorphite or smithsonite.

Chalcopyrite (Copper Pyrites)

$CuFeS_2$ Tetragonal **Habit** Crystals often of tetrahedral appearance; usually massive. Contact, interpenetration, or lamellar twins. . **Colour** Brass-yellow, sometimes with iridescent tarnish; opaque. Metallic lustre. Greenish-black streak. **Occurrence** Very common copper mineral widespread in medium- to high-temperature hydrothermal veins. Chalcopyrite is the primary copper mineral of most 'porphyry-copper' deposits. Also found in pegmatites, schists and some contact metamorphic rocks. **Distinguishing properties** Colour and tarnish; S.G. 4.1–4.3; hardness $3\frac{1}{2}$–$4\frac{1}{2}$; poor cleavage; uneven fracture; brittle. Soluble in nitric acid. Distinguished from pyrite by lower hardness; gold by brittle character and pyrrhotine by colour and lack of magnetism.

Wurtzite

ZnS Hexagonal **Habit** Found a pyramidal crystals, also occurs radia ing, fibrous massive. **Colour** Brownis black; opaque to translucent. Resinou lustre. Brown streak. **Occurrenc** Rather rare; an unstable high tem perature modification of sphalerit (stable above 1020°C) with which often occurs intergrown; usually foun in sulphide ores formed from acidi fluids. **Distinguishing properties** Habi S.G. 4.0–4.1; hardness $3\frac{1}{2}$–4; distinc prismatic cleavage; even to conchoida fracture.

Greenockite

CdS Hexagonal **Habit** Occurs rarely as pyramidal crystals, usually as a powdery coating. **Colour** Orange-yellow; translucent. Adamantine to resinous lustre. Orange-yellow to brick-red streak. **Occurrence** Most important cadmium mineral. Found as a yellow coating to zinc minerals such as sphalerite. Small crystals are found at several localities associated with prehnite and natrolite in cavities in basalts. **Distinguishing properties** Colour; habit; S.G. 4·9; hardness $3-3\frac{1}{2}$; distinct prismatic, imperfect basal cleavage; conchoidal fracture. Soluble in hydrochloric acid giving off hydrogen sulphide gas.

Pyrrhotine (Pyrrhotite, Magnetic Pyrites)

FeS Hexagonal. Usually shows a deficiency of iron, the formula varying from FeS to $Fe_{0\cdot8}S$. Troilite which has a composition close to the ideal FeS is found only in meteorites. **Habit** Mostly massive, granular, but occasionally as rosettes of hexagonal platy crystals. **Colour** Bronze-yellow, tarnishing to brown; opaque. Metallic lustre. Greyish black streak. **Occurrence** Occurs principally in basic igneous rocks such as gabbro, and as disseminated grains. Also found in pegmatites, in contact metamorphic deposits or high-temperature sulphide veins and replacement bodies. **Distinguishing properties** Colour; magnetic; S.G. 4·6–4·7; hardness $3\frac{1}{2}-4\frac{1}{2}$; basal parting; subconchoidal to uneven fracture. Distinguished from chalcopyrite by colour and magnetism and from pyrite by colour and hardness.

Nickeline (Niccolite)

NiAs Hexagonal **Habit** Occurs rarely as pyramidal crystals, usually massive in reniform or columnar aggregates. **Colour** Pale copper-red often alters on surfaces to pale green annabergite (nickel bloom). Metallic lustre. Pale brownish-black streak **Occurrence** Found with pyrrhotine, chalcopyrite and other nickel sulphides in basic igneous rocks; also in hydrothermal vein deposits with cobalt and silver minerals. **Distinguishing properties** Colour and alteration; S.G. 7·8; hardness 5–5½; lack of cleavage; uneven fracture. Soluble in nitric acid giving a green solution.

Millerite

NiS Hexagonal (Trigonal) **Hab** Usually as acicular needles, often radiating groups. **Colour** Brass yellow; opaque. Metallic lustre. Green ish black streak. **Occurrence** Fre quently as tufts of slender crystals i cavities in limestone or dolomite, ofte as an alteration product of othe nickel-rich minerals. As a late stag mineral in hydrothermal deposits. **Dis tinguishing properties** The fibrou yellow crystals of millerite with the characteristic metallic lustre are readil identifiable. S.G. 5·3–5·6; hardnes 3–3½; perfect rhombohedral cleavage uneven fracture.

Pentlandite

(Fe,Ni)$_9$S$_8$ Cubic **Habit** Massive, usually as granular aggregates. **Colour** Bronze-yellow; opaque. Bronze-brown streak. Metallic lustre. **Occurrence** The mineral is one of the most important ores of nickel. Usually found in basic igneous rocks with iron and nickel sulphides and arsenides, accumulated by magmatic segregation. Usually found intergrown with pyrrhotine. **Distinguishing properties** Not easily distinguished from pyrrhotine except in polished section. S.G. 4·6–5.0; hardness $3\frac{1}{2}$–4; lack of cleavage; conchoidal fracture.

Covelline (Covellite)

CuS Hexagonal **Habit** Crystals are rare, usually in hexagonal plates; mostly massive. **Colour** Indigo blue, often iridescent to brass-yellow or purplish-red; opaque except in very thin fragments. Metallic lustre. Dark grey to black streak. **Occurrence** Usually found in the zone of secondary enrichment with chalcosine, bornite and chalcopyrite formed by the alteration of primary sulphides. Also sometimes found in hydrothermal veins as a primary sulphide. **Distinguishing properties** Colour and perfect basal cleavage distinguish covellite from chalcosine and bornite. S.G. 4·6–4.8; hardness $1\frac{1}{2}$–2.

Cinnabar

HgS Hexagonal (Trigonal) **Habit** Crystals are usually rhombohedral or thick tabular, sometimes short prismatic; also granular, massive. Twinning is common with basal pinacoid as twin plane. **Colour** Scarlet-red to brownish red; transparent to translucent, occasionally opaque. Adamantine to submetallic lustre in opaque specimens. Vermilion streak. **Occurrence** Cinnabar is the most important mercury mineral. Usually found in veins or impregnations formed at low temperatures near recent volcanic rocks or hot springs. Associated with pyrite, stibnite and realgar. **Distinguishing properties** Colour; S.G. 8·0–8·2; hardness 2–2½; prismatic perfect cleavage; subconchoidal fracture; slightly sectile. In the zone of weathering cinnabar may alter to native mercury or mercurous chloride (calomel).

Realgar

AsS Monoclinic **Habit** Short prismatic crystals, striated parallel to their length also occurs as granular or massive aggregates. **Colour** Bright red-orange to orange-yellow; transparent to translucent. Resinous to greasy lustre. Red orange streak **Occurrence** In low temperature hydrothermal deposits associated with orpiment, stibnite and other arsenic minerals. Also in deposits from hot springs and as volcanic sublimate. **Distinguishing properties** Colour; S.G. 3.5; hardness 1½–2; Good pinacoidal cleavage; conchoidal fracture; sectile. Often associated with orpiment. Specimens should be kept in darkened container as the mineral disintegrates on exposure to light forming a yellowish powdery mixture of orpiment and arsenolite (As_2O_3).

rpiment

s_2S_3 Monoclinic **Habit** Rarely ccurs as short prismatic crystals, sually as foliated or granular masses ssociated with realgar. **Colour** emon-yellow to brownish-yellow; ansparent to translucent. Resinous) pearly lustre. Pale yellow streak. **)ccurrence** As a low temperature nineral formed in hydrothermal veins nd certain hot spring deposits, often ssociated with realgar from which it orms as an alteration product. **Disnguishing properties** Colour and ssociation with realgar; S.G. 3·5; ardness $1\frac{1}{2}$–2; one perfect cleavage; early lustre on cleavage surfaces.

Stibnite (Antimony Glance)

Sb_2S_3 Orthorhombic **Habit** Stout or slender elongated, prismatic crystals, striated parallel to their length, crystals are sometimes bent or twisted. Commonly found in aggregates of acicular crystals or as radiating or columnar masses, sometimes granular. **Colour** Lead-grey, sometimes with blackish to iridescent tarnish; opaque. Metallic lustre. Lead-grey streak. **Occurrence** The most common antimony mineral. Commonly found in low-temperature hydrothermal veins with quartz, also as replacement bodies in limestone and in certain hot spring deposits. Often associated with orpiment, realgar, galena, pyrite and cinnabar. **Distinguishing properties** Habit; S.G. 4·5–4·6; hardness 2; one perfect cleavage parallel to length of crystals; subconchoidal fracture. Melts readily, even in a match flame. Soluble in hydrochloric acid.

Bismuthinite (Bismuth Glance)

Bi_2S_3 Orthorhombic. Isostructural with stibnite **Habit** Prismatic to acicular crystals; usually massive, foliated or fibrous. **Colour** Lead-grey to tin-white, sometimes with an iridescent tarnish; opaque. Metallic lustre. Lead-grey streak. **Occurrence** Found in high-temperature hydrothermal veins associated with native bismuth, arseno-pyrite, quartz and other sulphides. **Distinguishing properties** Habit; S.G. 6·8; hardness 2; one perfect cleavage. Less flexible but more sectile than stibnite. Dissolves in nitric acid with a white precipitate on dilution.

Pyrite (Iron Pyrites)

FeS_2 Cubic **Habit** Crystals common cubic, also as pyritohedra. Cubic faces are often striated with the striations perpendicular to those on adjacent faces. Also found massive or as nodules. Fossils are often replaced by pyrite. Frequently twinned to for interpenetrant crystals. **Colour** Pale brass-yellow; opaque. Metallic lustre. Greenish or brownish black streak. **Occurrence** Pyrite is one of the most widely distributed sulphide minerals. It is present in igneous rocks as an accessory mineral or as segregations, common in hydrothermal veins, in replacement and contact metamorphic deposits. It occurs in black shale formed under anaerobic conditions. **Distinguishing properties** Colour lack of tarnish; S.G. 4·9–5·2; hardness 6–6½; poor cubic cleavage; conchoidal to uneven fracture. From chalcopyrite by hardness. Soluble in nitric acid insoluble in hydrochloric acid.

Marcasite

FeS$_2$ Orthorhombic **Habit** Crystals are commonly tabular; also massive, stalactitic or as radiating fibres. Twinning is common often repeated, producing 'spear-shaped' or 'cockscomb' like crystal groups. **Colour** Pale bronze-yellow; opaque. Metallic lustre. Greyish or brownish black streak. **Occurrence** Marcasite occurs most often in near surface deposits, deposited at lower temperatures than pyrite. Also in low-temperature hydrothermal veins with zinc and lead ores. Frequently found in sedimentary rocks limestones, especially chalk or clays often as concretions or replacing fossils. **Distinguishing properties** Colour; habit; distinctive spear-shaped twins; S.G. 4.8–4.9; hardness 6–6$\frac{1}{2}$; distinct prismatic cleavage; uneven fracture. Decomposes more readily than pyrite.

Cobaltite

CoAsS Cubic **Habit** Sometimes as cubes or pyritohedra or combinations of these forms, faces often striated as in pyrite; commonly massive. **Colour** Silver-white to steel-grey often with a reddish tinge; opaque. Metallic lustre. Grey-black streak. **Occurrence** In high-temperature hydrothermal veins associated with arsenopyrite, skutterudite and nickeline, also as disseminated grains in metamorphic rocks. **Distinguishing properties** Colour; S.G. 6·3; hardness 5$\frac{1}{2}$; perfect cubic cleavage; uneven fracture. Sometimes alters to pink erythrite (cobalt bloom).

Arsenopyrite (Mispickel)

FeAsS Monoclinic **Habit** As short prismatic crystals, faces often striated. Columnar crystals have a rhombic cross-section; granular or massive. Twinning is common on prism, as contact, penetration or as cruciform twins; forms pseudo-orthorhombic crystals. **Colour** Silver grey-white, often with a brownish tarnish; opaque. Metallic lustre. Greyish-black streak. **Occurrence** The most abundant arsenic mineral. Forms under moderately-high temperature conditions, occurring with gold-quartz veins and also ores of tin, tungsten and silver, with pyrite, chalcopyrite, sphalerite and galena. Also found in limestones, dolomites, gneisses and pegmatites. **Distinguishing properties** Colour; S.G. 5·9–6·2 (some cobalt often substitutes for iron); hardness $5\frac{1}{2}$–6; indistinct prismatic cleavage; uneven fracture.

Molybdenite

MoS_2 Hexagonal **Habit** Crystals a hexagonal, often tabular; common foliated or scaly masses, also granula massive. **Colour** Lead-grey sometime with bluish tinges, opaque. Metall lustre. Greenish-grey streak, bluish grey on paper. **Occurrence** The mo common molybdenum mineral. Four as an accessory mineral in som granites or pegmatites and in hydro thermal veins with scheelite, wolfra mite, topaz and fluorite. Also in conta metamorphic deposits with garne pyroxene, scheelite and pyrite. **Distinguishing properties** Can only b confused with graphite but its colou lustre and density are characteristi S.G. 4·6–4·7; hardness 1–$1\frac{1}{2}$; perfec basal cleavage; flexible laminae; sectil

Skutterudite, Smaltite (illustrated) and Chloanthite Series

The three minerals form an iso-morphous series with the general formula. (Co,Ni) As_{2-3} Cubic **Habit** crystals occur as cubes, octahedra or cubo-octahedra usually massive or granular. **Colour** Tin-white to silver-grey, iridescent or greyish tarnish; opaque. Metallic lustre. Black streak. **Occurrence** Found in medium-tem-perature hydrothermal veins, with cobaltite, nickeline, arsenopyrite, silver and bismuth. **Distinguishing properties** habit; S.G. 6·1–6·9, hardness $5\frac{1}{2}$–6; distinct cubic and octahedral cleav-ages; conchoidal to uneven fracture. High cobalt members yield erythrite on weathering, rarer high nickel members, green annabergite. Chemical tests are required to distinguish the group from arsenopyrite.

Pyrargyrite

Ag_3SbS_3 Hexagonal (Trigonal) **Habit** Usually in hexagonal prisms with pyramidal terminations; also massive, compact. Twinning is common, form-ing 'swallow-tail' crystal groups. **Colour** Deep red, darkens on exposure to light; translucent to nearly opaque, transparent in thin fragments. Ada-mantine lustre. Dark red streak. **Occurrence** Pyrargyrite and proustite are commonly called ruby silver ores. Found in low-temperature silver veins, one of the last primary minerals to crystallize. Associated with native silver, argentite, tetrahedrite, galena and sphalerite. **Distinguishing proper-ties** Can be confused with proustite but pyrargyrite has a deeper red colour. Its habit distinguishes it from cuprite. S.G. 5·8; hardness $2\frac{1}{2}$; distinct rhombo-hedral cleavage; conchoidal to uneven fracture.

Proustite

Ag_3AsS_3 Hexagonal (Trigonal) Isostructural with pyrargyrite. **Habit** Prismatic crystals, sometimes rhombohedral or scalenohedral; also massive, compact. Twinning is common. **Colour** Scarlet, darkens on exposure to light; transparent to translucent. Adamantine lustre. Bright red streak **Occurrence** Found together with pyrargyrite in silver veins, but is less common. **Distinguishing properties** Colour and streak; S.G. 5·6; hardness $2-2\frac{1}{2}$; distinct rhombohedral cleavage; conchoidal to uneven fracture. After heating proustite forms a malleable globule of silver whereas pyrargyrite gives a brittle globule.

Tetrahedrite (illustrated) — Tennantite

$(Cu_{12}Sb_4S_{13})$ - $(Cu_{12}As_4S_{13})$ Cub These are the end members of continuous solid-solution series which arsenic substitutes for antimor Iron also substitutes for some copp and silver is often present. **Ha** Crystals are commonly tetrahedr also massive, granular compact. Co tact or penetration twins on tetr hedron. **Colour** Dark grey to blac opaque. Metallic lustre. Brown black streak. **Occurrence** Tetr hedrite is commonly found in low-medium-temperature hydrotherm veins associated with copper, lea silver and zinc minerals, also found contact metamorphic deposits. Te nantite is not as common. **Di tinguishing properties** Habit ar colour; S.G. 4·6—5·1 (tetrahedri higher than tennantite); hardness 3—4 subconchoidal to uneven fractur Oxidizes to malachite and azurite.

nargite

u₃AsS₄ u_3AsS_4 Orthorhombic   **Habit** rystals are commonly striated prisms, tabular. Often massive; granular, laded or columnar. Occasionally forms tar-shaped trillings (three individuals). Colour   Dark grey to black; opaque. Metallic lustre. Black streak.   **Occurrence**   The mineral is found in vein nd replacement deposits formed at ow to medium temperatures associated vith chalcosine, bornite, covelline, yrite, sphalerite, galena, baryte and uartz. **Distinguishing properties** The abular striated crystals are very charcteristic. S.G. 4·4; hardness 3; perfect rismatic cleavage (present even in ranular specimens), pinacoidal disnct; uneven fracture. It fuses easily nd will melt in a match flame.

Bournonite

$PbCuSbS_3$ Orthorhombic   **Habit** Crystals are usually short prismatic or tabular; also occurs as massive or granular. Twinning is very common, repeated twinning produces cruciform or cog-wheel-like crystal aggregates. **Colour** Steel-grey to black; opaque. Metallic lustre (usually bright on the edges of cog-wheel twins, but dull on the broad flat faces). Grey to black streak. **Occurrence** Found in medium-temperature hydrothermal veins, associated with galena, tetrahedrite, sphalerite, chalcopyrite, pyrite and rarely stibnite. Highly prized specimens came from the Herodsfoot mine, Liskeard, Cornwall.   **Distinguishing properties** Habit of twinned crystals; S.G. 5·7–5·9; hardness $2\frac{1}{2}$–3; poor prismatic cleavage; subconchoidal to uneven fracture.

Boulangerite

$Pb_5Sb_4S_{11}$ Monoclinic **Habit** Elongated prismatic to acicular crystals; usually striated along the direction of elongation; often in fibrous masses. **Colour** Bluish lead-grey; opaque. Metallic lustre. Brownish grey streak. **Occurrence** In low- to medium-temperature hydrothermal veins, often associated with galena, stibnite, sphalerite, pyrite and other lead-antimony minerals; also with quartz, calcite and dolomite. **Distinguishing properties** Habit; S.G. 6·0–6·2; hardness $2\frac{1}{2}$–3; one good cleavage; generally brittle but thin fibres are flexible. Similar in physical properties to stibnite and jamesonite but it has a higher specific gravity than both of these minerals. X-ray study often required for positive identification.

Jamesonite

$Pb_4FeSb_6S_{14}$ Monoclinic **Hab** Acicular to fibrous crystals, striat along the direction of elongation; oft in felted masses; also massive, colur nar. **Colour** Grey black, sometim with iridescent tarnish; opaque. Meta lic lustre. Grey-black streak. **Occu rence** In medium-temperature hydr thermal veins, associated with oth sulphides and sulpho-salts. **Di tinguishing properties** Habit; S. 5·6 (lower than boulangerite); har ness 2–3; good basal cleavage. Di solves in hot hydrochloric acid givir the characteristic 'rotten egg' odour hydrogen sulphide. Crystals are n flexible like those of stibnite.

Oxides

Cuprite

Cu₂O Cubic **Habit** Crystals are usually small modified octahedra, sometimes cubes or dodecahedra, also fine acicular crystals (var. chalcotrichite); often massive, granular. **Colour** Dark red, sometimes nearly black (var. chalcotrichite – red fibres); translucent, sub-transparent when thin fragments. Adamantine to submetallic lustre. Brownish red streak. **Occurrence** Often found as a secondary mineral in the oxidized zone of copper sulphide deposits. **Distinguishing properties** Habit and colour; associated minerals; S.G. 6·1; hardness 3½–4 (softer than hematite and harder than cinnabar); poor octahedral cleavage; conchoidal to uneven fracture. Cuprite is soluble in hydrochloric acid staining the solution blue on dilution.

Zincite

ZnO Hexagonal **Habit** Crystals very rare (hexagonal pyramids); usually massive, foliated or granular. **Colour** Orange-yellow to deep red; translucent. Subadamantine lustre. Orange-yellow streak. **Occurrence** Zincite is a rare mineral except for a few localities such as Franklin, New Jersey, U.S.A. where it occurs in association with calcite, franklinite and willemite. **Distinguishing properties** Characteristic association; red colour and streak; S.G. 5·7; hardness 4; perfect prismatic cleavage; conchoidal fracture. Dissolves in hydrochloric acid.

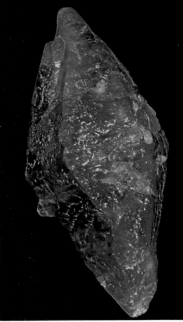

Franklinite

$(Zn,Mn,Fe)(Fe,Mn)_2O_4$ Cubic. A member of the spinel group (see page 48). **Habit** Crystals octahedral, also massive, granular. **Colour** Black; opaque. Metallic lustre. Reddish-brown to dark brown streak. **Occurrence** Franklinite, zincite and willemite occur together in the zinc deposits of Franklin, New Jersey. The deposits are associated with crystalline limestone and are probably of a metasomatic origin. **Distinguishing properties** S.G. 5·0–5·2; hardness $5\frac{1}{2}$–$6\frac{1}{2}$; lack of cleavage; uneven fracture. Slightly magnetic.

Corundum (Ruby, Sapphire)

Al_2O_3 Hexagonal (Trigonal) **Hab**▐ Crystals are commonly tabular; al▐ rough, steep pyramidal 'spindl▐ shaped' prismatic forms; also massi▐ granular. Emery is a mixture of granu▐ corundum, magnetite and spinel. Twi▐ ning is common, and often lamell▐ producing striations. **Colour** Bl▐ (sapphire), pink to red (ruby) al▐ yellow, brown, green, single cryst▐ sometimes show colour variatio▐ transparent to translucent. Adama▐ tine to vitreous lustre. White strea▐ **Occurrence** Most abundant in marb▐ schists and gneisses. In some pe▐ matites and certain nepheline syenite▐ Also in alluvial gravels as 'place▐ deposits. **Distinguishing properti**▐ Habit; S.G. 3·9–4·1; hardness 9 (gre▐ hardness); lack of cleavage; bas▐ parting; uneven to conchoidal fractur▐

Hematite

Fe_2O_3 Hexagonal (Trigonal) **Habit**
Crystals are often thin tabular, some-
mes as rosettes (iron rose); also
rombohedral with curved, striated
aces. Commonly massive. Compact
aggregates, often in characteristic
lamillated or botryoidal forms (kidney
re). Penetration twins on basal pina-
oid. **Colour** Steel-grey to black.
Massive compact varieties – dull to
right red; opaque. Metallic lustre. Red
o reddish brown streak. **Occurrence**
Hematite is the most important ore of
on and is widely distributed. Chiefly
ound in thick beds of sedimentary
rigin. In metamorphosed sediments
nd contact metamorphic deposits.
Distinguishing properties Colour and
treak; S.G. 4·9–5·3; hardness 5–6;
ack of cleavage; uneven fracture.
oluble in concentrated hydrochloric
cid.

Ilmenite

$FeTiO_3$ Hexagonal (Trigonal) **Habit**
Crystals are commonly thick tabular;
often massive, compact. Twinning is
common on basal pinacoid. **Colour**
Iron-black; opaque. Metallic to submetallic lustre. Black streak. **Occurrence** Common accessory mineral in
igneous rocks such as gabbros, diorites
and anorthosites. Also found in ore
veins and pegmatites, and as alluvial
or beach sands. The mineral is an
important source of the metal titanium.
Distinguishing properties S.G. 4·8;
hardness 5–6; parting on basal plane;
conchoidal fracture; distinguished from
hematite by its black streak and from
magnetite by its lack of magnetism.

Braunite

$3Mn_2O_3.MnSiO_3$ Tetragonal **Habit**
Found mostly as pyramidal crystals;
also massive, granular crystals sometimes appear to be pseudo-octahedral.
Colour Brownish-black to steel-grey;
opaque. Submetallic lustre. Brownish-
black to steel-grey streak. **Occurrence**
Often found in hydrothermal veins with
other manganese oxides, also formed
as the product of metamorphism of
manganese bearing sediments. **Distinguishing properties** Colour and
crystal form. S.G. 4·7–4·8; hardness
$6-6\frac{1}{2}$; perfect pyramidal cleavage; uneven fracture. Soluble in hydrochloric
acid, leaving a residue of silica.

Rutile

TiO_2 Tetragonal **Habit** Crystals com
monly prismatic, faces often striate
sometimes acicular, rarely pyramida
also massive, granular. Twinning
common on bipyramid, forming knee
shaped twins, or complex cyclic twir
made up of 6 or 8 individuals. Colo
Usually reddish-brown to red, some
times black (iron-, tantalum-, and nic
bium-bearing); transparent to trans
lucent, black specimens opaqu
Adamantine to metallic lustre. Pa
brown streak. **Occurrence** Widesprea
accessory mineral in igneous rock
also in quartzites, schists and gneisse
Also concentrated in alluvial deposi
and beach sands. Often occurs a
acicular crystalline inclusions in quart
Distinguishing properties Colou
habit and twinning; S.G. 4·2–5·
(niobium and tantalum varieties
hardness $6-6\frac{1}{2}$; distinct prismat
cleavage; uneven fracture.

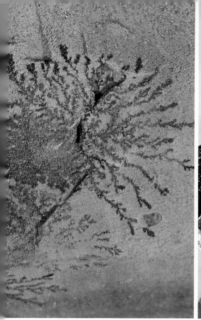

Pyrolusite

MnO_2 Tetragonal **Habit** Crystals are rare, sometimes found in form of elongated prisms. Usually occurs in reniform sooty masses which soil the hands when touched. Also very common as dendritic encrustations (see illustration above) in narrow fissures. **Colour** Dark grey; opaque. Metallic to dull lustre. Black streak. **Occurrence** Pyrolusite is a secondary mineral formed by the oxidation of manganite and other primary manganese minerals. Often found associated with hausmannite, braunite, goethite and limonite. **Distinguishing properties** Habit. Dissolves in conc. hydrochloric acid giving off chlorine gas. Only distinguishable from psilomelane if crystals are visible. S.G. 5·06 for crystals, lower when massive; hardness $6–6\frac{1}{2}$ for crystals, massive 2–6; perfect prismatic cleavage; uneven fracture.

Cassiterite (Tinstone)

SnO_2 Tetragonal **Habit** Crystals are usually short prismatic or pyramidal; also massive, granular. Also as fibrous botryoidal crusts or masses (wood tin) or waterworn pebbles (stream tin). Twinning is common forming contact and penetration twins, often repeated. **Colour** Usually reddish brown to nearly black; nearly transparent to opaque. Adamantine and splendant lustre. White or light grey to brown streak. **Occurrence** A high temperature mineral occurring in hydrothermal veins and pegmatites closely associated with granitic rocks. Commonly associated with wolframite, arsenopyrite, topaz, quartz and tourmaline. Abundant in some alluvial deposits. **Distinguishing properties** Habit and colour; lustre and streak; S.G. 7·0; hardness 6–7; imperfect prismatic cleavage; subconchoidal to uneven fracture.

Anatase (Octahedrite)

TiO_2 Tetragonal **Habit** Crystals commonly bipyramidal; also tabular. **Colour** Various shades of yellow and brown, deep blue or black; transparent to nearly opaque. Adamantine lustre. White to pale yellow streak. **Occurrence** As an accessory mineral in igneous and metamorphic rocks. Formed at relatively low temperatures and frequently found in veins or fissures in schists and gneisses. Commonly associated with quartz, brookite and rutile. Occasionally in granite pegmatites. Also as a detrital mineral. **Distinguishing properties** Habit and colour; S.G. 3·8–4·0; hardness $5\frac{1}{2}$–6; perfect basal and pyramidal cleavages; subconchoidal fracture.

Brookite

TiO_2 Orthorhombic **Habit** Crystals are usually thin tabular, platy prismatic. **Colour** Reddish-brown brownish-black; translucent. Metall to adamantine lustre. White to yello streak. **Occurrence** As an accesso mineral in igneous and metamorph rocks and in hydrothermal veins whe it forms at relatively low temperature Often found as detrital grains. **Distinguishing properties** Habit an colour; S.G. 4·1; hardness $5\frac{1}{2}$–6; poo prismatic cleavage; subconchoidal t uneven fracture. Rutile, anatase an brookite are polymorphs of TiO_2.

Tungstite (Tungsten Ochre)

$WO_3.H_2O$ Orthorhombic **Habit** Occasionally found as microscopic platy crystals; generally massive, earthy. **Colour** Yellow to yellowish green; translucent. Resinous lustre. Yellow streak. **Occurrence** Usually formed by the oxidation of wolframite and is usually found associated with it in tungsten deposits. **Distinguishing properties** Colour and association with wolframite. S.G. 5·5; hardness $2\frac{1}{2}$; perfect basal cleavage.

Uraninite (Pitchblende)

UO_2 Cubic **Habit** Crystals are rare, cubic with octahedral modifications. Usually occurs as massive, botryoidal (pitchblende) or earthy. **Colour** Brownish-black or greyish-black; opaque. Submetallic to greasy or pitch-like lustre; dull. Brownish-black or greyish streak. **Occurrence** Crystallized uraninite occurs in some granite and syenite pegmatites, associated with zircon, tourmaline, monazite, mica and feldspar. Pitchblende is usually found as colloform crusts in high- to medium-temperature hydrothermal veins with cassiterite, pyrite, chalcopyrite, arsenopyrite and galena. Also as a detrital mineral in some sedimentary quartz conglomerates. **Distinguishing properties** Habit; lustre; S.G. 8–10 (crystals), 6·6–8·5 (massive); hardness 5–6; conchoidal to uneven fracture. Bright yellow or green alteration patches. Highly radioactive.

Brucite

$Mg(OH)_2$ Hexagonal (Trigonal) **Habit** Crystals usually broad tabular; commonly foliated massive, fibrous or fine granular. **Colour** White to pale grey, pale green or blue; transparent to translucent. Pearly lustre on cleavage surfaces, waxy to vitreous elsewhere. White streak. **Occurrence** In metamorphosed dolomitic limestones and also as a low-temperature hydrothermal mineral, often found in veins in serpentine. Usually associated with calcite, aragonite, talc and magnetite. **Distinguishing properties** Foliated habit and lustre; S.G. 2·4; hardness $2\frac{1}{2}$; perfect basal cleavage; separable, flexible plates; sectile. Easily soluble in hydrochloric acid. Distinguished from talc by greater hardness and from gypsum by habit.

Lepidocrocite

$FeO(OH)$ Orthorhombic **Habit** A tabular or scaly crystals; usually a micaceous, fibrous or massive aggregates. **Colour** Red to brown; transparent. Submetallic lustre. Dull orang streak. **Occurrence** Found as secondary mineral, usually associate with goethite. **Distinguishing proper ties** Colour and streak; S.G. 3.9–4.1 hardness 5; perfect cleavage; brittl fracture.

Manganite

MnO(OH) Monoclinic (pseudo-thorhombic) **Habit** Crystals prismatic, often striated and with blunt or flat terminations. Frequently grouped in bundles, also columnar to coarse fibrous. Contact or penetration twins in prism. **Colour** Black to dark grey; opaque. Submetallic lustre. Reddish brown to black streak. **Occurrence** In low-temerature hydrothermal veins, associated with granite rocks. Deposited in bogs, lakes, and shallow marine environments. Often found associated with pyrolusite, geothite and baryte. **Distinguishing properties** habit; colour and streak; S.G. 4·3; hardness 4; perfect pinacoidal cleavage; uneven fracture. Soluble in concentrated hydrochloric acid, liberating chlorine gas. Infusible.

Bauxite

Bauxite is the name given to deposits rich in hydrous aluminium oxides. It is mostly a mixture of gibbsite, boehmite and diaspore. Bauxite occurs as massive, oolitic, pisolitic or earthy concretionary masses. Formed by prolonged tropical weathering and leaching of silica from rocks containing aluminium silicates.

Gibbsite (Hydrargillite) (illustrated) $Al(OH)_3$ Monoclinic **Habit** Tabular crystals, usually massive as botryoidal, stalactitic encrustations, also foliated and earthy aggregates. Twinning is common. **Colour** White, grey, sometimes pink or red; transparent to translucent. Vitreous lustre, pearly on cleavages. White streak **Occurrence** in earthy or pisolitic bauxite. Also as a low-temperature hydrothermal mineral in aluminous igneous rocks. **Distinguishing properties** S.G. 2·4; hardness $2\frac{1}{2}$–$3\frac{1}{2}$; perfect basal cleavage.

Boehmite

AlO(OH) Orthorhombic **Habit** Microscopic tabular crystals; commonly disseminated or pisolitic aggregates. **Colour** White, dull, earthy lustre. White streak. **Occurrence** An important constituent of bauxite, formed by the weathering of aluminium silicate rocks low in quartz. **Distinguishing properties** Needs microscopic identification. S.G. 3·0–3·1; hardness 3; one good cleavage.

Diaspore (illustrated)

AlO(OH) Orthorhombic **Habit** Crystals commonly thin platy, prismat also massive, foliated and scaly aggr gates. **Colour** White to colourles sometimes green, pink or brow transparent to translucent. Vitreo lustre, pearly on cleavages. White strea **Occurrence** Massive material occu in bauxite deposits. With corundum emery deposits, or as a hydrotherm alteration product of other alumino minerals. **Distinguishing properti** Habit; S.G. 3·3–3·5; hardness $6\frac{1}{2}$– one perfect cleavage; conchoic fracture.

Wad is a mixture of several hydro manganese oxides, such as pyrolusi (p. 41) and psilomelane (p. 47 Similar in appearance to both thes minerals and found in deposits forme in lakes and bogs under highly oxidizir conditions.

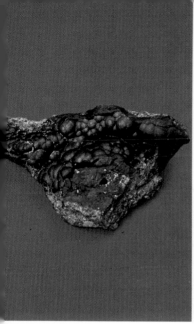

silomelane

Monoclinic. Psilomelane is one of a number of hydrous manganese oxides often occurring as a mixture of fine-grained or earthy botryoidal masses. The name is now applied to the mineral in which barium is an important constituent (cryptomelane with potassium, and coronadite where lead predominates) **Colour** Black to dark grey; opaque. Submetallic to dull lustre. Brownish black streak. **Occurence** A secondary mineral precipitated at atmospheric temperatures together with pyrolusite, goethite, and limonite. Often forms as residual deposit resulting from the weathering of manganese carbonates or silicates. Concretionary forms common in lake and swamp deposits. **Distinguishing properties** Botryoidal, concretionary appearance; streak; S.G. 4·4—4·7; hardness 5—7 (lower for earthy material).

Goethite (illustrated)

FeO(OH) Orthorhombic **Habit** Crystals are platy, bladed or prismatic, usually massive, stalactitic, botryoidal or radiating fibrous; sometimes earthy. **Colour** Dark brown to yellowish-brown; opaque. Adamantine to dull lustre. Often silky due to fibrous structure. Brownish-yellow streak **Occurrence** As a secondary mineral, found in the oxidation zone of veins containing iron minerals. Also formed as a direct precipitate in bogs or lagoons. **Distinguishing properties** Colour; habit; S.G. 3·3—4·3; hardness 5—5½; one perfect cleavage; uneven fracture. Sometimes magnetic after strong heating.

Limonite is an impure hydrated iron oxide, largely composed of goethite. Brown coloured, with a yellow-brown streak. Found mainly as botryoidal or weathered crusts, formed by the oxidation of iron minerals or as a precipitate in bog or marine deposits.

Spinel

$MgAl_2O_4$ Cubic A series of minerals of similar structure, which includes $MgAl_2O_4$ (spinel) $FeAl_2O_4$ (hercynite) $ZnAl_2O_4$ (gahnite) $MnAl_2O_4$ (galaxite). **Habit** Crystals are usually octahedral; also massive. Twinning is common on octahedron (spinel twins). **Colour** Variable; commonly red (ruby spinel) but also blue, green, brown, black to colourless; transparent (magnesium-rich) to opaque. Vitreous lustre. White streak (spinel); grey (gahnite); green (hercynite); red-brown (galaxite). **Occurrence** As an accessory mineral in igneous rocks. In metamorphosed aluminous schists and in contact metamorphosed limestones in which gem quality spinels occur; also in alluvial deposits derived from these. **Distinguishing properties** Habit and twinning; S.G. 3·5–4·1; hardness $7\frac{1}{2}$–8; octahedral parting; conchoidal to uneven fracture. Infusible.

Magnetite

Fe_3O_5 Cubic. A member of the spin group. **Habit** Commonly as octahedr crystals, also dodecahedral, often ma sive, granular. Twinning is common o octahedron (spinel twins). **Colo** Black; opaque. Metallic to submetall lustre. Black streak. **Occurrence** As a abundant and widely distributed oxic mineral. Commonly found as an acces sory mineral in igneous rocks, and a magmatic segregation deposits wit pyroxene and apatite. It is a commo mineral in contact and regional metamorphosed calcareous rocks wit garnet, diopside, pyrite and chalcopy rite, also in some high-temperatur mineral veins. Also as a detrital miner in beach or river sands. **Distinguishir properties** Habit and colour; strea S.G. 5·2; hardness $5\frac{1}{2}$–$6\frac{1}{2}$; octahedr parting; subconchoidal to uneve fracture. Strongly magnetic.

hromite

Cr_2O_4 Cubic. A member of the inel group, often contains some agnesium (magnesio-chromite) or uminium. **Habit** Crystals are rare ut octahedral; usually massive, granu-r. **Colour** Black; opaque. Metallic stre. Brown streak. **Occurrence** As accessory mineral in igneous rocks uch as peridotite and serpentinite, in ese it is often concentrated into yers or lenses. Also found in alluvial nds or gravels. Chromite is the sole urce of chromium metal which is idely used in the production of ainless steels. **Distinguishing proper-es** Brown streak and weak magnetism stinguishes chromite from magnetite. G. 4.1–5.1; hardness $5\frac{1}{2}$; uneven acture. Infusible.

Chrysoberyl (Alexandrite)

$BeAl_2O_4$ Orthorhombic **Habit** Crystals are usually tabular or short prismatic; also granular massive. Contact or penetration twins are common, often repeated forming pseudo-hexagonal crystals. **Colour** Green, yellow sometimes brownish; transparent to translucent. The transparent gem variety alexandrite is green in natural light but red by artificial light. A further gem variety, usually yellow-green, contains many fine, fibrous inclusions causing chatoyancy, 'cat's-eye', in polished samples. Vitreous lustre. White streak. **Occurrence** In granite pegmatites, also in mica schists. Frequently found in alluvial deposits. **Distinguishing properties** Habit and twinning; colour; S.G. 3·7–3·8; hardness $8\frac{1}{2}$; distinct prismatic cleavage; conchoidal to uneven fracture.

49

Pyrochlore (illustrated) and Microlite

$(Ca,Na)_2(Nb,Ta)_2O_6)O,OH,F)$ Cubic. Substitution for sodium and calcium occurs including uranium, thorium and rare earth elements. **Habit** Crystals commonly octahedral, also in irregular masses and as embedded grains. **Colour** Pyrochlore — various shades of brown to black; microlite — pale yellow to brown, sometimes shades of red or green; subtranslucent to opaque. Vitreous to resinous lustre. Streak is paler than its colour. **Occurrence** Usually found in pegmatites associated with alkaline igneous rocks, with zircon and apatite, tantalite and columbite. Pyrochlore is also found in igneous intrusions of carbonatite. Microlite is usually associated with granite pegmatites. **Distinguishing properties** Crystal form; colour; S.G. 4·2 (pyrochlore) to 5·5 (microlite); hardness 5–5½; distinct octahedral cleavage; subconchoidal to splintery fracture. Some specimens are radioactive due to uranium and thorium.

Columbite (illustrated) — Tantalite Series

$(Fe,Mn)(Nb,Ta)_2O_6$
$(Mn,Fe)(Ta,Nb)_2O_6$ Orthorhomb[ic]. **Habit** Occurs as short or equa[nt] prismatic crystals, sometimes thin [or] thick tabular, may also form lar[ge] groups of subparallel crystals; al[so] massive. Twinning is common, usua[lly] as simple contact twins; also as r[e]peated twins. **Colour** Iron-black [to] brownish black; reddish brown in th[in] splinters. Often an iridescent surfa[ce] tarnish; subtranslucent to opaque. Su[b]metallic to resinous lustre. Dark red [to] black streak. **Occurrence** Usually as [a] primary mineral in granite pegmatite[s]. Also found in some detrital 'plac[er] deposits. **Distinguishing properti[es]** Colour; crystal form; S.G. 5·2 (colum[bite) to 8.0 (tantalite); hardness [6] (columbite) to 6½ (tantalite); distin[ct] pinacoidal cleavage; subconchoidal [to] uneven fracture.

alides

alite (Rock Salt)

aCl Cubic **Habit** Cubic crystals often
th hollow faces (hopper crystals);
so massive and granular. **Colour**
alourless or white, also shades of
allow, red and blue (due to the
essence of impurities); transparent to
anslucent. Vitreous lustre. White
reak. **Occurrence** Halite is widely
stributed in stratified beds formed
the evaporation of saline waters in
closed basins. Thick deposits of
alite associated with sylvine, gypsum
ad anhydrite occur in sedimentary
asins. Also occurs as a volcanic
blimate. **Distinguishing properties**
abit and transparency; S.G. 2·1—2.2;
ardness 2½; perfect cubic cleavage;
anchoidal fracture; salty taste; soluble
water.

Sylvine

KCl Cubic **Habit** Usually as cubic
crystals sometimes octahedral; also
massive, compact. **Colour** Colourless
or white, also shades of grey, blue,
yellow or red; transparent to translucent. Vitreous lustre. White streak.
Occurrence Found in bedded salt-
deposits such as those at Stassfurt,
Germany and associated with, but less
common than halite because of its
greater solubility in water. Also found
as encrustations in volcanic fumaroles
especially at Mount Vesuvius. **Distinguishing properties** S.G. 2·0; hardness 2; perfect cubic cleavage; uneven
fracture. Bitter taste.

Carnallite

$KMgCl_3.6H_2O$ Orthorhombic **Habit** Crystals are rare, sometimes pseudo-hexagonal or tabular; usually massive or granular. **Colour** Colourless to white, often red-orange due to minute hematite inclusions; transparent to translucent. Greasy, dull to shiny lustre. White streak. **Occurrence** In the upper-layers of evaporite deposits together with halite and sylvine. Together with sylvine the mineral is mined and used as a source of potassium for fertilizers. **Distinguishing properties** S.G. 1.6; hardness $2\frac{1}{2}$. Distinguished from other salts by the lack of cleavage; conchoidal fracture. Deliquescent; soluble in water. Bitter taste. Fuses readily when heated.

Fluorite (Fluorspar)

CaF_2 Cubic **Habit** Crystals usua cubic, sometimes octahedral or rhom dodecahedral; also massive, coarse fine granular or compact. Interper trant twins common. **Colour** Colo less when pure, commonly purp blue, green, yellow or brown, rare pink or red. Blue-john is a massiv colour banded variety; transparent translucent. Vitreous lustre. Wh streak. **Occurrence** Commonly hydrothermal veins, particularly tho associated with galena and sphaler quartz and baryte. Also in son greisens, granites and high-tempe ature cassiterite veins. **Distinguishir properties** Habit; S.G. 3.2; hardness perfect octahedral cleavages; su conchoidal to splintery fracture. La of effervescence with hydrochlor acid. Generally weakly fluorescent.

Cryolite

Na_3AlF_6 Monoclinic **Habit** Crystals are rare, sometimes pseudocubic in appearance; usually massive, coarsely granular. Twinning is very common, complex. **Colour** Colourless to white, also reddish and brownish; transparent to translucent. Vitreous to greasy lustre. White streak. **Occurrence** Found in major quantities at only a few localities. At Ivigtut in Greenland it occurs in a pegmatitic body associated with microcline, quartz, siderite, galena and fluorite. It was formally used as a flux in the electrolytic production of aluminium, but the synthetic compound is now generally used. **Distinguishing properties** Pseudocubic habit; lustre; S.G. 3·0; hardness $\frac{1}{2}$; basal and prismatic parting, to give cuboidal form. Fuses readily when heated.

Chlorargyrite (Horn Silver, Cerargyrite)

AgCl Cubic **Habit** Crystals cubic, but rare; commonly massive as waxy or horn-like masses. Twinning is on octahedral planes. **Colour** Colourless when fresh, usually grey becoming violet-brown on exposure to light; translucent. Resinous to adamantine lustre. White streak. **Occurrence** Secondary mineral occurring in the oxidized zones of silver deposits, especially in arid regions. Commonly associated with native silver, cerussite and limonite. **Distinguishing properties** Colour; S.G. 5·5—5·6; hardness $1\frac{1}{2}$—$2\frac{1}{2}$; uneven to subconchoidal fracture; sectile and ductile. Melts readily when heated giving a silver globule.

Atacamite

$Cu_2(OH)_3Cl$ Orthorhombic **Habit** Commonly in slender, striated, prismatic crystals, sometimes tabular; also massive, fibrous or granular. Twinning occurs sometimes as doublets, trillings and other complex twins. **Colour** Bright green to dark green; transparent to translucent. Adamantine to vitreous lustre. Apple-green streak. **Occurrence** Found as a secondary mineral in the oxidized zone of copper deposits especially in arid, saline conditions. Often associated with malachite, cuprite, chrysocolla, brochantite, gypsum and limonite. **Distinguishing properties** Habit and colour; S.G. 3·8; hardness 3–3½; perfect pinacoidal cleavage; conchoidal fracture. Distinguished from malachite by lack of effervescence in hydrochloric acid.

Mendipite (illustrated with vein chloroxiphite)

$Pb_3O_2Cl_2$ Orthorhombic **Habit** Crystals bladed or fibrous; sometime massive. **Colour** Colourless to wh or brownish grey; transparent to tran lucent. Pearly lustre on cleavage resinous elsewhere. White strea **Occurrence** Found in the mangane deposits of the Mendip Hills, Somerse England. **Distinguishing properti** S.G. 7·2; hardness 2½; perfect pri matic cleavage and two other goo cleavages; conchoidal to unev fracture.

Chloroxiphite

$Pb_3CuCl_2O_2(OH)_2$ Monoclinic **Hab** Bladed crystals in subparallel group **Colour** Olive-green; translucer Resinous to adamantine lustre. Pa yellow-green streak. **Occurrence** Ra secondary mineral associated wi mendipite. **Distinguishing properti** S.G. 6·9–7·0; hardness 2½; one perfe and one distinct cleavage.

Carbonates

Calcite

CaCO$_3$ Hexagonal (Trigonal). Calcite the stable form of CaCO$_3$ at most temperatures and pressures. Manganese and iron may substitute for calcium. **Habit** Crystals common and very varied. Four habits are common: tabular, prismatic, rhombohedral, and calenohedral (dog tooth spar). Many combinations of these types may be found as well as fibrous, granular, stalactitic or massive aggregates. Twinning is common, usually the twin plane is either the basal pinacoid or a rhombohedral face. Lamellar twinning may also be produced by pressure. **Colour** Colourless (transparent) or white (opaque) when pure; often yellow or brownish (containing iron) pinkish (containing manganese or cobalt) also green, red, purple, blue, and black. Generally transparent to translucent. Vitreous lustre. White streak. **Occurrence** Very common, and found in many different environments. Often the major constituent of calcareous sedimentary rocks (lime-

stone, chalk) and metamorphic rocks (marble). It may be precipitated directly from sea-water or as the material forming shells of living organisms which on death accumulate to form limestone. It is commonly found in veins associated with metallic ores. Sometimes replaces primary minerals in igneous rocks. Formed as a deposit of travertine or tufa from hot and cold calcareous springs. Stalactites and stalagmites are often formed of calcite. **Distinguishing properties** Habit; S.G. 2·7 (pure); hardness 3; perfect rhombohedral cleavage, despite the variable habit; conchoidal fracture. Effervesces freely in cold dilute hydrochloric acid. Infusible. Many specimens also fluoresce in ultraviolet light due to impurities.

Magnesite

$MgCO_3$ Hexagonal (Trigonal) **Habit** Crystals rare, but rhombohedral or prismatic; usually massive or granular, may be compact or fibrous. **Colour** White or colourless when pure, often grey, brown or yellowish when iron-bearing; transparent to translucent. Vitreous to earthy lustre. White streak. **Occurrence** Formed by the alteration of rocks consisting largely of magnesium silicates and by waters rich in carbonate. Found as stratiform beds of metamorphic origin with talc-chlorite or mica schists, also as a replacement of calcite rocks by magnesium bearing solutions. **Distinguishing properties** S.G. 3·0–3·2; hardness $3\frac{1}{2}$–$4\frac{1}{2}$; perfect rhombohedral cleavage; conchoidal fracture. Distinguished from dolomite and calcite by S.G. and lack of twinning. Will dissolve with effervescence in warm hydrochloric acid.

Siderite (Chalybite)

$FeCO_3$ Hexagonal (Trigonal) **Hal** Crystals commonly rhombohedral, fr quently with curved or compos faces; also massive, granular, compa or fibrous. Twinning on rhombohedro often lamellar. **Colour** Grey to yellow ish brown; transparent to transluce Vitreous lustre. White streak. **Occu rence** Widespread as bedded depos in sedimentary rocks, these are oft impure containing clays (clay-iro stone), carbonaceous material (blac band iron-ores) or calcium carbona Nodules of siderite are common clay or shales. Also found as a gang mineral in hydrothermal veins. **Di tinguishing properties** Crystal forr from other rhombohedral carbonat by colour; S.G. 3·8–4·0; hardne $3\frac{1}{2}$–$4\frac{1}{2}$; perfect rhombohedral cleavag uneven fracture. Soluble in hot hydr chloric acid with effervescence.

Rhodochrosite

MnCO₃ Hexagonal (Trigonal). Calcium and iron commonly substitute for
manganese. **Habit** Crystals rhombohedral, rarely scalenohedral, usually
with curved faces; mostly massive,
compact or granular. **Colour** Pale to
deep rose pink, yellowish grey, brownish; transparent to translucent. Vitreous
lustre. White streak. **Occurrence** In
low-temperature hydrothermal veins
containing ores of silver, lead and
copper. Sometimes found in high-
temperature metasomatic deposits with
garnet and rhodonite, and as a second-
ry mineral in residual or sedimentary
manganese oxide deposits. **Distinguishing properties** From other
rhombohedral carbonates by colour;
S.G. 3·5–3·7; hardness 3½–4; perfect
rhombohedral cleavages; uneven fracture. Dissolves with effervescence in
hot, dilute hydrochloric acid.

Smithsonite (Calamine)

ZnCO₃ Hexagonal (Trigonal). Iron and
manganese may substitute for some
zinc. **Habit** Crystals rare, but rhombohedral with rough, curved faces. Usually as botryoidal, reniform or stalactitic
masses; also granular to compact, earthy
or porous cavernous masses. **Colour**
Shades of grey, brown or greyish-
white also green, brown and yellow;
translucent. Vitreous lustre. White
streak. **Occurrence** Found in the
oxidized zone of most zinc-ore
deposits. It may also be found replacing calcareous rocks adjacent to
the ore deposits. Usually associated
with hemimorphite, cerussite, malachite, anglesite, and pyromorphite.
Distinguishing properties Habit; S.G.
4·3–4·5 (high for a carbonate); hardness 4–4½; perfect rhombohedral
cleavage (when observed); uneven
fracture. Soluble in warm hydrochloric
acid with effervescence. Infusible.

Dolomite

$CaMg(CO_3)_2$ Hexagonal (Trigonal).
Iron often substitutes for magnesium.
Habit Crystals commonly rhombohedral, with curved composite faces
'saddle-shaped'; also massive, coarse
to fine granular, columnar and compact. Twinning is common, especially
on basal plane and rhombohedron.
Colour Colourless, usually white, often
yellow, brown or pinkish; transparent
to translucent. Vitreous to pearly lustre.
White streak. **Occurrence** Common as a
rock-forming mineral. Most 'sedimentary' dolomite results from the action
of magnesium-rich solutions on pre-
existing limestones. Occurs in hydrothermal veins with fluorite, baryte,
siderite and calcite. Also as veins in
serpentine, talcose rocks and altered
basic igneous rocks. **Distinguishing
properties** Habit; colour; S.G. 2·8–2·9;
hardness $3\frac{1}{2}$–4; perfect rhombohedral
cleavage; subconchoidal fracture. Re-
acts less readily with cold dilute hydrochloric acid (compare calcite) but
effervesces readily when warm.

Ankerite

$Ca(Mg,Fe)(CO_3)_2$ Hexagonal (Trigonal). There is a series from dolomi[te]
to ankerite with iron substituting f[or]
magnesium. **Habit** Crystals a[re]
rhombohedral; also massive, granula[r.]
Twinning is common, similar to dolomite. **Colour** White, yellow, yellowish
brown sometimes grey, becomes da[rk]
brown on weathering or increasin[g]
iron content; translucent. Vitreou[s]
lustre. White streak. **Occurrence** Ofte[n]
found as a gangue mineral in sulphid[e]
veins especially associated with iro[n]
ores. Frequently fills joints in co[al]
seams. **Distinguishing propertie[s]**
Colour; S.G. 2·9–3·2; hardness $3\frac{1}{2}$–[4;]
perfect rhombohedral cleavage.

ragonite

ₐCO₃ Orthorhombic **Habit** Crystals ₄ort to long prismatic, also acicular, ᵗten found in radiating groups; also ₙiform, globular or stalactitic. Un-ᵥinned crystal are rare; repeated ᵥinning results in pseudo-hexagonal ₒrms of both contact and penetration ₚes. **Colour** Colourless, white, grey, ₑllowish, sometimes violet; trans-ₐrent to translucent. Vitreous lustre. ᵥhite streak. **Occurrence** Main ₒmponent of the shells of many ᵣganisms (corals and oysters). As the ᵣimary precipitate of calcium car-ₒnate from sea-water. As a deposit of ₒt springs often found with gypsum. ₗso in the oxidized zone of some ore ₑposits. **Distinguishing properties** .G. 2·9; hardness 3½–4; distinct ᵢnacoidal cleavage; subconchoidal ₐcture. Dissolves with effervescence ᵢ cold dilute hydrochloric acid.

Witherite

BaCO₃ Orthorhombic **Habit** Crystals always twinned, often repeatedly twinned giving pseudo-hexagonal forms; also massive, granular, colum-nar or botryoidal. **Colour** Colourless, grey-white, pale yellow to brown; transparent to translucent. Vitreous lustre. White streak. **Occurrence** In some low-temperature hydrothermal veins associated with baryte and galena. **Distinguishing properties** Habit; S.G. 4·3; hardness 3–3½; distinct pinacoidal cleavage; uneven fracture. Soluble in dilute hydrochloric acid with effervescence. Powdered witherite will colour a flame apple-green (barium) readily distinguishing the mineral from strontianite (red).

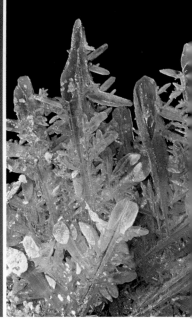

Strontianite

$SrCO_3$ Orthorhombic **Habit** Prismatic crystals, often acicular and radiating; also massive, fibrous, columnar or granular. Contact twins common, often repeated to give pseudohexagonal forms. **Colour** Colourless, white, yellow, pale-green or brownish; transparent to translucent. Vitreous lustre. White streak. **Occurrence** Usually as a low-temperature hydrothermal mineral often associated with celestine, baryte and calcite. Also as concretionary masses in limestones or clay. **Distinguishing properties** Habit; S.G. 3·7; hardness $3\frac{1}{2}$–4; nearly perfect prismatic cleavage; uneven fracture. Soluble with effervescence in dilute hydrochloric acid. When powdered it colours a flame red (strontium).

Cerussite

$PbCO_3$ Orthorhombic **Habit** Crysta are common, often prismatic or tabu parallel to side, pinacoid, sometim bipyramidal or pseudohexagonal form also massive, granular, compact a sometimes stalactitic. Twinning is ve common, may be multiple, formi reticulated groups, star-shape pseudohexagonal crystals or arrov head twins. **Colour** Usually white grey, sometimes darker colours due impurities; transparent to transclucer Adamantine lustre. White strea **Occurrence** A common seconda mineral found in the oxidized zone ore deposits containing galena. **Di tinguishing properties** Twinned form lustre; S.G. 6·4–6·6; hardness 3–3 Distinct prismatic cleavage in tw directions; conchoidal fracture. Di solves with effervescence in war dilute nitric acid.

Malachite

$_2CO_3(OH)_2$ Monoclinic **Habit** Crystals rare, almost always found as botryoidal, stalactitic or encrusting masses. Often with a structure of compact radiating fibres, banded in various shades of green; also granular earthy. Twinning is common. **Colour** Bright green, various shades; translucent. Fibrous varieties have silky lustre, rather dull when massive, crystals adamantine. Pale-green streak. **Occurrence** Common secondary copper mineral, often occurring in the oxidized zone of copper deposits. It may be found as pseudomorphs after azurite or cuprite. **Distinguishing properties** Habit; colour; S.G. 3·9—4·0 (some massive varieties as low as 3·6); hardness $3\frac{1}{2}$—4; perfect cleavage (rarely seen); subconchoidal to uneven fracture. Soluble with effervescence in dilute hydrochloric acid.

Azurite (Chessylite)

$Cu_3(CO_3)_2(OH)_2$ Monoclinic **Habit** Crystals often tabular or short prismatic, frequently complex in habit and malformed in development; also in radiating groups, massive or earthy. **Colour** Various shades of azure-blue; transparent to translucent. Vitreous to adamantine lustre. Pale-blue streak. **Occurrence** Found as a secondary copper mineral in the oxidized zone of copper deposits, often interbanded with malachite. Also associated with chrysocolla, chalcosine, calcite, limonite and other secondary copper minerals. **Distinguishing properties** Distinct crystals are common. Colour; S.G. 3·8; hardness $3\frac{1}{2}$—4; perfect prismatic cleavage, also pinacoidal; conchoidal fracture. Dissolves with effervescence in dilute hydrochloric acid. Frequently alters to malachite.

Leadhillite

$Pb_4(SO_4)(CO_3)_2(OH)_2$ Monoclinic
Habit Crystals often pseudo-
hexagonal, thin to thick tabular occasionally prismatic or equant; also
massive, granular. Twinning is very
common, of several different types to
give pseudohexagonal, lamellar and
interpenetrant twins. **Colour** Colourless, white, grey, pale green, blue and
yellow; transparent to translucent.
Resinous to adamantine lustre. White
streak. **Occurrence** Found in the
oxidized zone of lead deposits as a
secondary mineral associated with
cerussite, anglesite, lanarkite, linarite,
pyromorphite and galena. **Distinguishing properties** Habit and twinning;
S.G. 6·5–6·6; hardness $2\frac{1}{2}$–3; perfect
basal cleavage, splits into flexible
plates; conchoidal fracture. Dissolves
with effervescence in nitric acid leaving
a residue of lead sulphate. Breaks up in
hot water.

Aurichalcite

$(Zn,Cu)_5(OH)_6(CO_3)_2$ Orthorhomb
Habit As delicate acicular or slend
lath-like crystals. Commonly as tuft
aggregates or encrustations, rare
columnar, granular. **Colour** Pale gre
to greenish-blue, sky-blue; trar
parent. Silky to pearly lustre. Pa
green or blue streak. **Occurren**
Widespread as a secondary mineral
the oxidized zone of zinc-copp
deposits, rarely in pegmatites. **D**
tinguishing properties Habit; colo
S.G. 3·9–4·2; hardness 1–2; one pe
fect cleavage. Dissolves in hydr
chloric and nitric acids.

trates and Borates

ratine (Chile Saltpetre,
da Nitre)

NO$_3$ Hexagonal (Trigonal) **Habit** stals are rare, rhombohedral; usually ssive or granular, often as enstations. Twinning is common. **our** Colourless or white, sometimes dish-brown, grey or yellowish; nsparent to translucent. Vitreous tre. White streak. **Occurrence** Comnly found in arid regions as surface osits, associated with gypsum, ite and other soluble nitrates and phates. **Distinguishing properties** bit; S.G. 2·2–2·3; hardness 1–2; fect rhombohedral cleavage; conoidal fracture. Dissolves easily and npletely in water. Deliquescent. ses easily giving bright-yellow ission (sodium).

Nitre

KNO$_3$ Orthorhombic **Habit** As thin encrustations or silky acicular crystals. Twinning is often multiple, forming pseudohexagonal twins. **Colour** White; translucent. Vitreous lustre. White streak. **Occurrence** Occurs with nitratine, as friable crusts on surface rocks. Also as a constituent of certain soils. The important deposits in Chile are exploited as a source of nitrates. **Distinguishing properties** Habit; S.G. 2·1; hardness 2; perfect cleavage. Dissolves easily in water but not deliquescent. Fuses easily with violet emission (potassium).

Borax

$Na_2B_4O_7.IOH_2O$ Monoclinic **Habit** Crystals usually short prismatic; also massive. **Colour** Colourless or white, sometimes with tinges of blue, green or grey; translucent. Vitreous lustre. White streak. **Occurrence** Found in evaporite deposits, precipitated by the evaporation of salt lakes in arid regions. In association with other evaporite minerals such as halite, as well as sulphate and carbonate minerals and other borates. **Distinguishing properties** Habit; S.G. 1·7; hardness $2–2\frac{1}{2}$; perfect pinacoidal cleavage; conchoidal fracture. Easily fusible, with swelling. Colours a flame yellow (sodium). Soluble in water.

Colemanite

$Ca_2B_6O_{11}.5H_2O$ Monoclinic **Ha** Crystals are often highly modified b usually short prismatic; also massiv compact and granular. **Colo** Colourless white or grey; transpare to translucent. Vitreous to adamanti lustre. White streak. **Occurrence** As lining to cavities or geodes in sec mentary rocks formed as a seconda mineral derived from waters passi through primary borate deposits, su as borax and ulexite. **Distinguishi properties** S.G. 2·4; hardness 4–4 one perfect cleavage; uneven fractu Soluble in hot hydrochloric acid, wi the separation of a white precipita (boric acid) on cooling. Fuses easily

exite

$CaB_5O_9.8H_2O$ Triclinic   **Habit**
ually in rounded masses of fine
rous crystals (cotton balls) or as
rallel fibrous aggregates; rare as
ongate crystals. **Colour** Colourless
rystals) to white; transparent to
nslucent. Vitreous lustre (crystals),
ky (aggregates). White streak.
ccurrence   An evaporite mineral
curring with borax in the surface
posits of arid areas. Also found in
me bedded gypsum deposits **Dis-**
guishing properties   Habit; S.G.
9–2·0; hardness $2\frac{1}{2}$ (aggregated
aterial has an apparent hardness of
; perfect cleavage (crystals). Fuses
sily in candle flame with swelling.
rtually insoluble in cold water, slightly
luble in hot. Tasteless.

Kernite

$Na_2B_4O_7.4H_2O$ Monoclinic   **Habit**
Usually found as coarse cleavable
aggregates; crystals often stubby sometimes wedge-shaped, rounded and
markedly striated. **Colour** Colourless,
but usually chalky white due to
surface alteration film of tincalconite
$(Na_2B_4O_7.5H_2O)$; transparent. Vitreous to pearly lustre. White streak.
Occurrence Found in a large deposit
in the Mojave Desert of California,
United States. Believed to have formed
from an existing borax deposit by
subsequent recrystallization caused by
increased temperature and pressure.
Distinguishing properties S.G. 1·9–
2.0; hardness $2\frac{1}{2}$–3; two perfect cleavages, giving long splintery fragments.
Slowly dissolves in cold water; readily
dissolves in hot water.

Sulphates

Baryte (Barytes, Barite)

$BaSO_4$ Orthorhombic.   Strontium substitutes for barium in solid solution series from baryte to celestine. **Habit** Crystals commonly tabular, often diamond shaped due to the development of vertical prisms, elongated prismatic crystals common; also as globular concretions and fibrous, and in 'cockscomb' masses, as well as earthy aggregates. Some 'desert roses' are formed from rosettes of baryte crystals enclosing sand grains. **Colour** Colourless to white, often yellow, blue, green, red, or brown (due to impurities of iron minerals); transparent to translucent. Vitreous lustre. White streak. **Occurrence** Most common barium mineral, found mainly as a gangue mineral in metalliferous hydrothermal veins, associated with ores of lead, copper, zinc, silver and iron, together with quartz, fluorite and dolomite. Also in residual surface deposits, in hot springs deposits and in cavities in some igneous rocks. Also occurs as a replacement deposit in limestones and as veins, cement concretions in sedimentary rocks. Use primarily as a drilling mud for oil and gas wells. Also chief source of barium for chemicals. **Distinguishing properties** Habit; S.G. 4·5; hardness 3–3; perfect basal cleavage; prismatic, very good; uneven fracture. Insoluble in dilute acids. When powdered colours a flame apple-green (barium). Some specimens are fluorescent and phosphorescent in ultraviolet light.

lestine

SO₄ Orthorhombic **Habit** Crystals
ular or elongated prismatic, similar
baryte; also fibrous, granular and
ncretionary masses. **Colour** Colour-
s, white, pale blue, sometimes red-
>wn; transparent to translucent. Vit-
ous lustre. White streak. **Occurrence**
iefly occurs in sedimentary rocks,
rticularily dolomite. Associated with
ryte, gypsum, halite, dolomite and
orite. Occurs also with anhydrite in
aporite deposits. Often found as-
ciated with sulphur in some volcanic
as. Occurs as a gangue mineral in
drothermal veins with galena and
halerite. **Distinguishing properties**
bit; S.G. 3·9–4·0; hardness 3–3½;
rfect basal and good prismatic
eavage; uneven fracture. Insoluble in
ute acids. Colours a flame crimson
rontium).

Anglesite

$PbSO_4$ Orthorhombic **Habit** Crystals
often tabular, sometimes elongated
prismatic or pyramidal; also massive,
compact and granular. Concentrically
banded massive varieties sometimes
enclose an unaltered core of galena.
Colour Colourless to white, grey, pale
shades of yellow, blue or green;
transparent to opaque. Adamantine
lustre when pure. White streak. **Occurrence** Common secondary mineral,
most commonly found in the oxidized
zone of lead deposits associated with
galena, cerussite and other secondary
lead minerals and silver halides.
Distinguishing properties Lustre;
association with galena; S.G. 6·2–6·4;
hardness 3;˙ good basal and distinct
prismatic cleavage; conchoidal fracture. Does not effervesce in acids.
Small fragments will fuse in a candle
flame.

Anhydrite

$CaSO_4$ Orthorhombic **Habit** Crystals not common; usually massive, fibrous or granular. Sometimes as contorted concretionary forms. **Colour** Colourless or white when pure, often grey or reddish, frequently shows a bluish tinge; transparent to translucent. Vitreous to pearly lustre on cleavage. White streak. **Occurrence** Important rock forming mineral, found in bedded evaporite deposits. May be deposited directly from sea-water or formed by the dehydration of gypsum. Also found as a product of hydrothermal alteration of limestones and dolomites, or as a gangue mineral in hydrothermal metallic-ore veins **Distinguishing properties** S.G. 2·9–3·0; hardness $3–3\frac{1}{2}$; three good pinacoidal cleavages at right angles, forming rectangular cleavage fragments; uneven fracture. Does not dissolve readily in dilute acids.

Gypsum

$CaSO_4.2H_2O$ Monoclinic **Habit** Crytals usually simple in habit; prisma tabular parallel to side, pinacoid oft with curved faces; also granular, ma sive fibrous (satin spar). The f grained granular variety is called a baster. Twinning is very comme giving 'swallow-tail' or 'arrow-he types as well as simple twins, often radiating interpenetrating grou **Colour** Colourless to white (colourle transparent variety is selenite), gr sometimes yellow or brownish; tran parent to translucent. Vitreous lust pearly parallel to cleavage. Wh streak. **Occurrence** Gypsum is fou in extensive sedimentary deposits us ally interbedded with limestones, san stones and halite. As such it is the fi salt precipitated from an evaporati brine, and is followed by anhydrite a halite. Also formed as a seconda mineral deposited from percolati ground-waters replacing other se mentary rocks (some 'desert roses' a gypsum crystal rosettes enclosing sa

Epsomite (Epsom Salt)

$MgSO_4.7H_2O$ Orthorhombic **Habit** Rarely found as natural crystals; usually in botryoidal masses and fibrous crusts. **Colour** Colourless to white; transparent to translucent. Vitreous lustre, fibrous types silky to earthy. White streak. **Occurrence** As encrusting masses on the walls of caves and mine workings, where rocks rich in magnesium have been exposed. Also formed from some mineral waters and in volcanic fumaroles. **Distinguishing properties** Fibrous habit; occurrence; S.G. 1·7; hardness $3\frac{1}{2}$—4; one perfect cleavage; conchoidal fracture. Readily soluble in water, bitter taste.

ains). Fine solitary crystals are found some calcareous muds or clays in sociation with the decomposition of rite. Also occurs where a limestone s reacted with volcanic vapours, and a gangue mineral in metallic veins. ed in the production of plaster of ris and as a filler. **Distinguishing** operties Habit; S.G. 2·3; Hardness 2 an be scratched with fingernail); one rfect cleavage, yielding thin flexible ates and two other distinct cleavages ring rhombic fragments. Dissolves hot dilute hydrochloric acid.

Alunite

$KAL_3(SO_4)_2(OH)_6$ Hexagonal (Trigonal) **Habit** As small rare crystals with the rhombohedra and basal pinacoid present giving pseudocubic appearance; usually massive **Colour** White, sometimes grey, yellow or reddish; transparent to translucent. Vitreous to pearly lustre. White streak. **Occurrence** Alunite is usually found as a secondary mineral in near surface rocks of volcanic regions, which have been altered by solutions bearing sulphuric acid. **Distinguishing properties** S.G. $2 \cdot 6 - 2 \cdot 8$; hardness $3\frac{1}{2}-4$; distinct basal cleavage; conchoidal fracture (crystals); uneven, splintery fracture (masses). Insoluble in water and practically insoluble in acids (slowly dissolves in sulphuric acid). Infusible. Difficult to distinguish from massive anhydrite, dolomite or magnesite without chemical or X-ray tests.

Jarosite (illustrated)

$KFe_3(SO_4)_2(OH)_6$ Hexagonal (Trigonal) **Habit** As crusts or coatings minute tabular or pseudocubic rhombhedral crystals; also granular, massi fibrous nodular and earthy. **Colc** Yellow ochre to dark brown. Vitrec to resinous lustre. Pale-yellow stre **Occurrence** As coatings on and a sociated with iron ores. Found as constituent of limonitic gossans. **D tinguishing properties** S.G. $3 \cdot 0 - 3$ hardness $2\frac{1}{2}-3\frac{1}{2}$; distinct basal clea age; uneven fracture.

Plumbojarosite

$PbFe_6(SO_4)_4(OH)_{12}$ Hexagonal (Triononal) **Habit** Minute tabular crysta compact masses, also earthy. **Colc** Dark brown. Dull to glistening lust Brown streak. **Occurrence** Seconda mineral found in the oxidized zones lead deposits. **Distinguishing prope ties** Habit; colour; associations; S. $3 \cdot 67$; hardness soft (talc-like).

narite

(Pb, Cu)$_2$SO$_4$(OH)$_2$ Monoclinic **Habit**
commonly prismatic, also tabular,
either as single crystals or as groups
and crusts of radiating aggregates.
Twinning is common. **Colour** Deep
blue; translucent. Vitreous lustre, pale-
blue streak. **Occurrence** A rare but
distinctive secondary mineral, found
in the oxidized zone of some lead-
copper ores. **Distinguishing properties**
colour; association; S.G. 5·3–5·4;
hardness 2½–3; perfect pinacoidal,
distinct basal cleavage; conchoidal
fracture. Distinguished from azurite by
the lack of effervescence with dilute
hydrochloric acid.

Brochantite

Cu$_4$SO$_4$(OH)$_6$ Monoclinic **Habit**
Crystals are stout prismatic to acicular,
also tabular. Commonly as drusy crusts
and aggregates of crystals, massive,
granular. Twinning is common, forming
pseudo-orthorhombic forms. **Colour**
Emerald-green to blackish-green, pale
green; transparent to translucent. Vitreous lustre, pearly on cleavage. Pale-
green streak. **Occurrence** As a
secondary mineral in the oxidized zone
of copper deposits, especially in arid
regions, but of worldwide occurrence.
Distinguishing properties Colour;
habit; association; S.G. 4·0; hardness
3½–4; perfect cleavage; conchoidal to
uneven fracture. Soluble in hydrochloric and nitric acids.

Crocoite

$PbCrO_4$ Monoclinic **Habit** Usually prismatic or acicular crystals, often striated, with brilliant faces, crystals sometimes hollow; also massive columnar or granular. **Colour** Bright orangered, various shades to brown; translucent. Adamantine to vitreous lustre. Orange-yellow streak. **Occurrence** A rare secondary mineral found in the oxidized zone of lead-chromium veins, together with other secondary lead minerals such as cerussite and pyromorphite. **Distinguishing properties** Habit; colour and lustre; S.G. 5·9–6·1; hardness $2\frac{1}{2}$–3; distinct prismatic cleavage; conchoidal to uneven fracture. Easily fusible.

Wolframite

$(Fe,Mn)WO_4$ Monoclinic. Virtually complete substitution series exists from ferberite $(FeWO_4)$ to hubnerit $(MnWO_4)$. **Habit** Crystals tabular prismatic to long prismatic. Often form bladed, striated subparallel group also found massive, granular. Commo as simple contact twins. **Colour** hubnerite is reddish brown to browr ish black, wolframite is brownish blac ferberite is black; translucent to opaqu Generally sub-metallic lustre. Reddish brown to brownish-black strea **Occurrence** Found in quartz veins an pegmatites associated with metall ores. Also found in high-temperatur hydrothermal veins. Occurs in som alluvial deposits. **Distinguishing proper ties** Colour; S.G. 7·0–7·5 (increase with iron content); hardness $4–4\frac{1}{2}$; or perfect cleavage; uneven fractur Ferberite is weakly magnetic.

heelite

WO$_4$ Tetragonal **Habit** Crystals ually bipyramidal, often with striated es, sometime tabular; also massive, nular. Twinning is common, usually penetration twins. **Colour** Colours to white, usually pale yellow, also enish, grey, brownish or reddish oloured tints usually due to molybnum content); transparent to transent. Vitreous to adamantine lustre. ite streak. **Occurrence** Often companies wolframite in pegmatites d high-temperature hydrothermal ns. Associated with cassiterite, lybdenite, fluorite and topaz. Also und in some contact metamorphic posits with garnet, axinite, idocrase d wollastonite. **Distinguishing perties** Pyramidal habit; colour; G. 5·9–6·1; hardness 4½–5; good ramidal cleavage; uneven fracture. ost scheelite will fluoresce under raviolet light.

Wulfenite

$PbMoO_4$ Tetragonal **Habit** Crystals usually square tabular plates, sometimes very thin, short prismatic or stubby, more rarely bipyramidal; also massive, coarse to fine granular. **Colour** Yellow, orange-red, grey, white, olive-green to brown, transparent to translucent. Vitreous to adamantine lustre. White streak. **Occurrence** Found as a secondary mineral formed in the oxidized zone of deposits of lead and molybdenum minerals, commonly associated with vanadinite, cerussite, anglesite and pyromorphite. **Distinguishing properties** Tabular crystals; colour and lustre; association; S.G. 6·5–7·0; hardness 3; distinct pyramidal cleavage; subconchoidal to uneven fracture. Fuses readily.

Phosphates and Arsenates
Xenotime

YPO_4 Tetragonal. Other rare-earth elements may substitute for yttrium. **Habit** Crystals short to long prismatic, also equant and pyramidal, closely resembling zircon with which it is often found in parallel growth. Sometimes occurs as radial aggregates of coarse crystals. **Colour** Yellow to reddish-brown, also greyish-white, pale yellow; translucent to opaque. Resinous to vitreous lustre. Pale-brown streak. **Occurrence** As a minor accessory mineral in granite and alkaline igneous rocks occurring as larger crystals in the associated pegmatites. Also occurs in some gneisses. **Distinguishing properties** Crystal form; S.G. 4·4–5·1; hardness 4–5 (c.p. zircon $7\frac{1}{2}$); perfect prismatic cleavage; uneven fracture.

Monazite

$(Ce, La, Th)PO_4$ Monoclinic Ha Crystals usually small, often tabular short prismatic. Faces are sometin rough, uneven and striated. Twinni is common, both as contact and per tration (cruciform) twins. Col Yellowish-or reddish-brown to brov also green; subtranslucent to su transparent. Resinous to waxy lust Streak is white or pale shades of abo **Occurrence** As an accessory mine in granitic and associated pegmati rocks Also in gneissic metamorph rocks. Detrital sands derived fr these rocks often contain considerab commercial quantities of monaz **Distinguishing properties** Crystal for S.G. 4·6–5·4 (mostly around 5); har ness 5–5$\frac{1}{2}$; distinct pinacoidal cleava also basal parting; uneven fractu Infusible.

vianite

$_3(PO_4)_2.8H_2O$ Monoclinic **Habit**
ystals usually prismatic, sometimes
ttened and blade-like in radiating
oups; also as reniform or encrusting
asses often with a fibrous structure.
ometimes powdery and earthy.
olour Colourless and transparent
hen fresh, becoming green, pale to
rk blue by oxidation; transparent to
anslucent. Vitreous lustre, pearly
arallel to cleavage. White or pale-blue
reak, rapidly changing to dark blue
brown. **Occurrence** As a secondary
ineral in the oxidized zone of metallic
e deposits containing iron sulphides
so in weathered zones of phosphate-
ch pegmatites, and in sedimentary
cks especially those containing
rganic matter. **Distinguishing proper-
es** Colour and streak; S.G. 2.6–2.7;
ardness $1\frac{1}{2}$–2; one perfect cleavage,
in cleavage plates flexible. Easily
oluble in acids.

Amblygonite

$(Li,Na)Al(PO_4)(F,OH)$ Triclinic **Habit**
As small crystals which are short
prismatic to equant, larger crystals
rough and ill-formed; also massive,
compact, commonly as cleavable
masses. Lamellar twinning common
Colour White to creamy white, also
pale shades of green, blue, pink or
yellow; translucent to transparent.
Vitreous to greasy lustre. White streak.
Occurrence Found in granite pegmatites together with other lithium-and
phosphate-rich minerals. **Distinguishing properties** Association; S.G. 3·1;
hardness $5\frac{1}{2}$–6; one perfect and one
good cleavage; Uneven to subconchoidal fracture. Not easily soluble in
acids. Fragments fuse easily and colour
a flame red (lithium). Varieties in
which hydroxyl is in excess of fluorine
are common and are called monte-
brasite.

Apatite

$Ca_5(PO_4)_3(F,Cl,OH)$ Hexagonal **Habit** Crystals common, short to long prismatic, sometimes tabular; also massive, granular. Occasionally globular or reniform, earthy or nodular. **Colour** Usually in shades of green to grey-green, also white, blue, green, violet, or reddish; transparent to translucent. Vitreous lustre. White streak. **Occurrence** An accessory mineral in a wide range of igneous rocks, including pegmatites and high-temperature hydrothermal veins, in both regional and contact metamorphic rocks especially in metamorphosed limestones. Also in sedimentary rocks as bedded marine-deposits. Apatite is the principal inorganic constituent of bone and teeth. **Distinguishing properties** Habit; S.G. 3·1–3·3; hardness 5; imperfect basal cleavage; conchoidal to uneven fracture. Dissolves in hydrochloric acid.

Pyromorphite

$Pb_5(PO_4)_3Cl$ Hexagonal. Arser substitutes for phosphorous and complete series extends to mimeti **Habit** Crystals usually of simp prismatic form, often in rounded barre shaped forms (campylite); also hollo often globular, reniform, granul **Colour** Various shades of green a brown, also orange-yellow and re rarely colourless; subtransparent translucent. Resinous to adamanti lustre. White or yellowish-white strea **Occurrence** A secondary mine found in the oxidized zone of le deposits, associated with other le minerals. Crystals are sometimes zon with the outer parts tending to mim tite. **Distinguishing properties** Hab colour and lustre; S.G. 6·5–7·1; har ness 3½–4; poor prismatic cleavag subconchoidal to uneven fracture. D solves in hydrochloric and nitric aci

imetite

$_5(AsO_4)_3Cl$ Hexagonal **Habit**
ystals are similar to those of pyro-
orphite, commonly simple hexagonal
rms of prismatic habit, also as the
rved barrel-shaped crystals, also
obular (campylite); sometimes as
tryoidal crusts. **Colour** Pale yellow
yellow-brown, orange-yellow;
insparent to translucent. Resinous to
amantine lustre. White streak.
ccurrence As a secondary mineral
ccurring in the oxidized zone of
senic-bearing lead-deposits often
sociated with pyromorphite, galena,
iglesite and hemimorphite. **Dis-
iguishing properties** Crystal form;
lour and lustre; S.G. 7·0—7·2; hard-
ss 3½—4; subconchoidal fracture.
ssolves in hydrochloric acid. Difficult
distinguish from pyromorphite with-
it chemical tests.

Vanadinite

$Pb_5(VO_4)_3Cl$ Hexagonal **Habit** Crystals are usually short to long prismatic,
also acicular, sometimes as hollow
prisms; also as rounded forms, globules
and in subparallel groupings. **Colour**
Orange-red, brownish-red to shades of
brown and yellow; subtransparent to
nearly opaque. Resinous lustre. White
to yellowish streak. **Occurrence** As a
secondary mineral found in the oxidized
zone of ore deposits containing galena
and other sulphides. It is found associated with pyromorphite, wulfenite,
cerussite, anglesite and linarite. **Distinguishing properties** Habit; Colour
and lustre; S.G. 6·7—7·1; hardness 3;
uneven to conchoidal fracture. Easily
fusible. Dissolves in hydrochloric acid
giving a green solution with a whitish
precipitate.

Turquoise

$CuAl_6(PO_4)_4(OH)_8.5H_2O$ Triclinic
Habit   Crystals are very rare, minute; usually massive, cryptocrystalline to fine-granular, as veinlets and crusts, stalactitic or concretionary shapes. **Colour**   Sky-blue, bluish-green to apple-green; transparent (crystals), to nearly opaque. Vitreous lustre (crystals) to waxy (massive). White or pale-green streak.   **Occurrence**   As a secondary mineral formed by the action of surface waters, usually in arid regions, on a aluminous igneous and sedimentary rocks. Usually forming in veins or irregular patches in the rock.   **Distinguishing properties**   Habit; colour; S.G. 2·6–2·8; hardness 5–6 (harder than chrysocolla); two good cleavages in crystals; massive material has a conchoidal fracture. It is fusible.

Erythrite (cobalt bloom) (illustrate and Annabergite (nickel bloom)

$Co_3(AsO_4)_2.8H_2O$ and
$Ni_3(AsO_4)_2.8H_2O$ Monoclinic. Cob and nickel substitute for one anoth to form a complete composition seri **Habit**   Crystals are usually prisma often acicular and flattened, sometim deeply striated and as radiating grou Commonly as globular or renifo shapes, earthy or powdery.   **Col** Erythrite,   crimson-red   and   pi (illustrated   above);   Annabergi apple-green; transparent to transluce Adamantine to dull lustre. Streak is colour but paler.   **Occurrence**   Secon ary minerals produced by the surfa oxidation of cobalt and nic arsenides in some ore deposits.   **D tinguishing properties**   Colour; asso ation with other cobalt-nickel miner is distinctive; S.G. 3·0–3·1; Hardne $1\frac{1}{2}$–$2\frac{1}{2}$; one perfect cleavage. Dissolv in acids.

orodite

$AsO_4.2H_2O$ Orthorhombic **Habit**
stals usually pyramidal and pseudo-
ahedral, also tabular or prismatic,
en forming crusts; also massive
dular or earthy. **Colour** Pale green,
e-green to blue, brown; transparent
translucent. Vitreous to adamantine
tre. White streak. **Occurrence**
ually found as a secondary mineral
gossans formed by the alteration of
enic minerals, especially arseno-
ite. **Distinguishing properties**
bit; association with arsenic
erals; S.G. 3·1–3·3; hardness $3\frac{1}{2}$–4;
erfect prismatic cleavage; sub-
choidal fracture. Dissolves in
drochloric and nitric acids.

Torbernite (illustrated) and Metatorbernite

$Cu(UO_2)_2(PO_4)_2.8–12H_2O$ Tetragonal.
At atmospheric temperatures torbernite
loses some of its water and tends to
form metatorbernite. **Habit** Crystals
are often square, thin to thick tabular;
also as foliated or scaly aggregates.
Colour Bright emerald-green to grass-
green; transparent to translucent. Vitreous lustre, pearly parallel to cleavage.
Streak is paler than colour. **Occurrence**
Found as a secondary mineral in the
oxidized zone of veins containing copper minerals and uraninite usually
associated with other secondary uranium minerals. **Distinguishing properties**
Crystal form; colour; S.G. 3·2 (torbernite) increasing to 3·7 (metatorbernite); hardness $2–2\frac{1}{2}$; perfect basal
cleavage, producing thin brittle
cleavage plates. Dissolves in hydrochloric and nitric acids. Does not
fluoresce.

Autunite (Meta-autunite)

$Ca(UO_2)(PO_4)_2.10-12H_2O$ Tetragonal
Habit Crystals occur as square, thin to thick tabular crystals; also as foliated or scaly aggregates, sometimes forming thick crusts of subparallel crystals. **Colour** Bright lemon to greenish yellow; transparent to translucent. Vitreous lustre. Yellow streak. **Occurrence** Found as a secondary mineral in the zone of oxidation and weathering, and hydrothermal veins and pegmatites rich in uraninite. **Distinguishing properties.** Crystal form; colour; S.G. 3·1–3·2; hardness 2–2½; perfect basal cleavage; producing thin cleavage plates less brittle than torbernite. Dissolves in hydrochloric and nitric acids. Fluoresces strongly (yellow-green) in ultraviolet light. Distinguished from yellow secondary uranium minerals by chemical or X-ray methods. Radioactive.

Carnotite

$K_2(UO_2)_2(VO_4)_2.3H_2O$ Monocli
Habit Rarely as minute, thin tabu crystals, usually as powdery or loo microcrystalline aggregates, sometin compact. **Colour** Bright yellow greenish yellow. Dull, earthy lus **Occurrence** As a secondary mine formed from circulating ground wat which have passed through deposits containing uranium and nadium minerals, generally disser nated through sandstones. Also fou as an alteration crust on some urani ores. **Distinguishing propert** Powdery habit; colour; S.G. 5 (wh fully hydrated); hardness ab 2; perfect basal cleavage. Easily d solves in hydrochloric and nitric aci Does not fluoresce (compare autunit

scloizite

(Zn,Cu)VO$_4$(OH) Orthorhombic.
compositional series exists due to
ostitution of copper for zinc to
ottramite (Pb(Cu,Zn)VO$_4$(OH)).
bit Crystals are prismatic, tabular or
dge-shaped, faces are usually un-
en or rough, subparallel growth is
mmon. Occurs commonly as crys-
line crusts; also mamillated with
rous radiating structure. **Colour**
ownish red to blackish brown, also
ange-red to nearly black; transparent
opaque. Greasy lustre. Orange to
ownish-red streak. **Occurrence** A
condary mineral occasionally found
the oxidized zone of some lead-zinc
posits. **Distinguishing properties**
ystal form; colour and streak; S.G.
9 (mottramite)–6.2 (descloizite);
rdness 3–4; uneven fracture. Easily
ssolves in hydrochloric or nitric
ids.

Olivenite

Cu$_2$AsO$_4$(OH) Orthorhombic **Habit**
Crystals prismatic or acicular, often
elongated, frequently occurs as globular and reniform shapes with a radiating
fibrous internal structure, also massive,
granular to earthy. **Colour** Shades of
olive-green to brown, but also paler
shades to greyish white; translucent to
opaque. Adamantine to vitreous lustre
Olive-green to brown streak. **Occurrence** As a secondary mineral found
in the oxidized zone of copper sulphide
deposits, associated with other copper
minerals. **Distinguishing properties**
Habit; colour and streak; S.G. 4·1–4·5;
hardness 3; poor cleavage; conchoidal
to irregular fracture. Dissolves in hydrochloric and nitric acids.

Libethenite

$Cu_2PO_4(OH)$ Orthorhombic **Habit** Crystals are short prismatic or equant; commonly composite and forming crusts. **Colour** Light to dark olive-green; transparent to translucent. Vitreous lustre. **Occurrence** A secondary mineral found in the oxidized zone of copper ore deposits, associated with other primary and secondary copper minerals. **Distinguishing properties** Colour; association; S.G. 3·9; hardness 4; very poor cleavage; conchoidal to uneven fracture. Easily dissolves in hydrochloric and nitric acids. Can be easily confused with olivenite.

Adamite

$Zn_2AsO_4(OH)$ Orthorhombic Cop may substitute for zinc to a consid able extent (cuproadamite). Ha Crystals usually small, and mere together in crusts or as roughly rad aggregates. **Colour** Commo yellowish-green, to brownish-yellc copper-bearing varieties are shades green, cobalt-bearing varieties viol rose; transparent to translucent. \ reous lustre. **Occurrence** A second mineral, found in the oxidized zone ore deposits, containing primary z and arsenic-rich minerals. Often e crusting limonite. **Distinguishi properties** Colour; S.G. 4·3–4 hardness $3\frac{1}{2}$; one good cleava uneven to subconchoidal fractu Easily dissolved in dilute acids. Sor specimens fluoresce lemon-yellow ultra-violet light.

roconite

$_2Al(AsO_4)(OH)_4.4H_2O$ Monoclinic
•bit Crystals are thin and wedge-
•aped, with some faces striated,
•en as subparallel groups, also
arsely granular. **Colour** Sky blue to
•een; transparent to translucent. Vit-
•ous to resinous lustre. Streak is paler
•an its colour. **Occurrence** A rare
•condary mineral found in the oxidized
•ne of copper deposits associated
•ith azurite, malachite, cuprite, oliven-
•, chalcophyllite and limonite.. **Dis-
•nguishing properties** Colour and
•sociation; S.G. 2·9–3·0; hardness
•-2½; indistinct cleavage; conchoidal
• uneven fracture. Easily dissolves in
•drochloric and nitric acids.

Chalcophyllite

$Cu_{18}Al_2(AsO_4)_3(SO_4)_3(OH)_{27}.33H_2O$
Habit Crystals are thin tabular, six-
sided forms; sometimes striated; also
as foliated masses or rosettes. **Colour**
Emerald green, also bluish-green;
transparent to translucent. Vitreous to
adamantine lustre. Pale-green streak.
Occurrence As a rare secondary
mineral in the oxidization zone of
copper-bearing ore deposits associated
with other copper minerals. **Distinguishing properties** Habit and
colour; S.G. 2·6–2·7; hardness 2;
perfect basal cleavage, forming flexible
cleavage plates. Dissolves in hydrochloric and nitric acids. Alters readily to
chrysocolla.

Lazulite

$(Mg,Fe)Al_2(PO_4)_2(OH)_2$ Monoclinic
Scorzalite is a related mineral but with
iron predominating over magnesium.
Habit Crystals are commonly steep
pyramidal; also massive, compact to
granular. Twinning is common. **Colour**
Deep azure-blue, also paler shades of
blue; translucent. (gem varieties are
transparent). Vitreous lustre. White
streak. **Occurrence** A rare mineral
found in some metamorphic rocks, as
grains or masses especially in quartzites, also in granite-pegmatite. Found
associated with high-grade metamorphic minerals such as kyanite,
sillimanite, corundum, muscovite and
garnet. **Distinguishing properties**
Crystal form; colour; association; S.G.
$3 \cdot 1$; hardness $5\frac{1}{2}$–6; indistinct prismatic
cleavage; uneven to splintery fracture.
Lazulite is much more common than
scorzalite.

Wavellite

$Al_3(PO_4)_2(OH)_3 \cdot 5H_2O$ Orthorhomb
Habit Crystals are rare, usually occu
as hemispherical or globular aggregat
with a fibrous radiating internal stru
ture; also as crusts or stalactite
Colour Colourless to white, yello
green and brown; translucent. V
reous lustre. White streak. **Occurren**
As a secondary mineral found
joint surfaces and in cavities of lc
grade metamorphic rocks such
slates and in some sedimentary phc
phate rock deposits. Sometimes fou
in limonitic-ore bodies. **Distinguishi**
properties Habit; S.G. $2 \cdot 3$–$2 \cdot 4$; har
ness $3\frac{1}{2}$–4; good prismatic cleavag
uneven to subconchoidal fractu
Easily dissolves in most acids.

...ildrenite

...e,Mn)Al(PO$_4$)(OH)$_2$.H$_2$O Ortho-
...ombic **Habit** Crystals equant or
...ramidal to short prismatic (manga-
...se–rich variety, eosphorite: long
...smatic); also thick tabular, some-
...es platy. **Colour** Brown to
...llowish-brown. Rose-red (eosphor-
...); transparent to translucent. Vit-
...ous to resinous lustre. White streak.
...ccurrence A rare mineral, but
...metimes found as fine crystals in
...me hydrothermal vein deposits and
...granite pegmatites. **Distinguishing**
...operties Habit; colour; S.G. 3·2–3·3
...ildrenite) 3·0–3·1 (eosphorite);
...rdness 5; poor cleavage; subcon-
...oidal to uneven fracture.

Ludlamite

Fe$_3$(PO$_4$)$_2$.4H$_2$O Monoclinic **Habit**
Thin to thick tabular crystals, sometimes wedge-shaped; also massive,
granular. **Colour** Bright green to apple
green; translucent. Vitreous lustre.
Greenish-white streak. **Occurrence** As
a secondary mineral in the oxidation
zone of ore deposits and as an
alteration product of primary iron
phosphate minerals in some granite
pegmatites, often associated with
vivianite **Distinguishing properties**
Colour; S.G. 3·1–3·2; hardness 3½;
perfect cleavage.

Variscite and Strengite

Al(PO$_4$).2H$_2$O and Fe(PO$_4$).2H$_2$O
Orthorhombic **Habit** Crystals rare,
usually as nodules and crusts. **Colour**
Variscite — various shades of green.
Strengite — red or violet. White streak.
Occurrence Secondary phosphate
minerals found in near-surface
deposits. **Distinguishing properties**
Colour; variscite from Fairfield, Utah;
forms characteristic nodules.

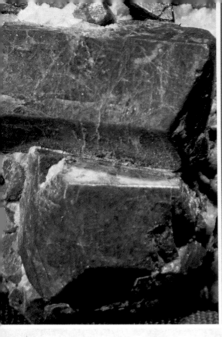

Silicates

The silicate minerals constitute almost a third of known mineral species and form over 90% of the Earth's crust. The feldspar minerals and quartz are the most common minerals in the Earth's crust.

Willemite

Zn_2SiO_4 Hexagonal (Trigonal) **Habit** Found as small prismatic or rhombohedral crystals; usually massive, granular. **Colour** Commonly pale greenish-yellow but varies from near white to dark brown; transparent to nearly opaque. Vitreous to resinous lustre. White streak. **Occurrence** Found in the oxidized zone of some zinc-ore deposits. Abundant in the ore deposit at Franklin, New Jersey. U.S.A. **Distinguishing properties** Colour; association; S.G. 3·9–4·2; hardness 5½; good basal cleavage. Willemite often shows strong fluorescence in ultra-violet light.

Phenakite

Be_2SiO_4 Hexagonal (Trigonal) **Ha** Crystals are often rhombohedral prismatic; also granular, and as acicu columnar aggregates. Twinning common. **Colour** Colourless, a white, yellow, pink and brown; tran parent to translucent. Vitreous lust **Occurrence** A rare beryllium mine found in cavities in granite and grani pegmatites in association with bet topaz and apatite, also found some hydrothermal veins. **Distinguis ing properties** Crystal form; S 3·0; hardness 7½–8; distinct prisma cleavage; conchoidal fracture.

ivine

1g,Fe)$_2$SiO$_4$ Orthorhombic   A
ntinuous solid solution series exists
tween two components Mg$_2$SiO$_4$
rsterite) and Fe$_2$SiO$_4$ (fayalite).
bit   Well-developed crystals rare,
ually occurs in granular masses or
isolated grains. **Colour** Olive-
en, also white (forsterite) and
wn to black (fayalite); transparent
translucent. Vitreous lustre. White or
y streak.   **Occurrence**   A rock
ming mineral, typical of basalt,
bbro and peridotite. Dunite is com-
sed entirely of olivine. Basalts oc-
sionally contain nodules of granular
vine and pyroxene. Forsteritic oli-
es are formed during the meta-
rphism of magnesium-rich sedi-
nts. Fayalite occurs in some pitch-
nes and slags.   **Distinguishing**
perties   Colour; association; S.G.
2 (forsterite)—4·4 (fayalite); hard-
ss 6½—7; indistinct pinacoidal cleav-
e; conchoidal fracture.

Humite Series

Mg(OH,F)$_2$.1–4Mg$_2$SiO$_4$ Orthorhombic and monoclinic The group com-
prises four minerals, norbergite, chondrodite, humite and clinohumite. They
differ in the amount of magnesia and
silica they contain. Humite and norbergite are orthorhombic, chondrodite
and clinohumite are monoclinic. **Habit**
Crystals are usually stubby, often highly
modified; also massive. **Colour** White,
pale yellow-brown; translucent. Vitreous to resinous lustre. **Occurrence**
Found typically in metamorphosed
dolomite limestones in association
with spinel, phlogopite, garnet, diopside and idocrase. **Distinguishing
properties** Habit; colour; association
with metamorphosed limestones; S.G.
3·1–3·3; hardness 6–6½; One poor
cleavage; uneven fracture.

Zircon

$ZrSiO_4$ Tetragonal **Habit** Crystals usually prismatic, with bipyramidal terminations. Twinning is common, forming knee-shaped twins. **Colour** Usually brown or reddish-brown, but sometimes found colourless, grey, green or violet; transparent to translucent. Vitreous to adamantine lustre. White streak. **Occurrence** A common accessory mineral in igneous rocks such as granite, syenite and nepheline syenites. In pegmatites, crystals sometimes reach a considerable size. Also found in metamorphic rocks such as schists and gneisses. Often as a detrital mineral in river and beach sands. **Distinguishing properties** Habit; colour; S.G. 4·6–4·7; hardness $7\frac{1}{2}$; indistinct prismatic cleavage; uneven to conchoidal fracture. Zircon is often radioactive due to thorium and uranium replacing zirconium.

Andalusite

Al_2SiO_5 Orthorhombic. Andalus sillimanite and kyanite are polymorp of Al_2SiO_5. **Habit** Crystals prisma nearly square in cross-section; a massive. The variety chiastolite exhib a cruciform pattern of carbonace(impurities when viewed in cro section. **Colour** Commonly pink red, also grey, yellow, brown a green; transparent to nearly opaq Vitreous lustre. White streak. **Occ rence** Found typically in therm metamorphosed argillaceous schi and in regionally metamorphosed roc formed under low pressure conditio Rarely found in some granite pe matites. **Distinguishing propert** Habit; association; S.G. 3·1–3·2; ha ness $6\frac{1}{2}$–$7\frac{1}{2}$; distinct prismatic cleavag uneven to subconchoidal fractu Readily alters to an aggregate of wh mica flakes which coat crystals.

Sillimanite (Fibrolite)

$_2SiO_5$ Orthorhombic **Habit** Commonly occurs as elongated prismatic crystals, striated along their length, even as fibrous or interwoven masses. **Colour** Colourless or white, yellow-brown or greenish; transparent to translucent. Vitreous lustre, often silky fibrous material. White streak. **Occurrence** Found typically in schists and gneisses produced by high-grade regional metamorphism. **Distinguishing properties** Fibrous habit resembling other fibrous silicates such as wollastonite and tremolite. For precise identification optical or X-ray tests are needed. S.G. $3 \cdot 2$–$3 \cdot 3$; hardness $6\frac{1}{2}$–$7\frac{1}{2}$; perfect prismatic cleavage. Infusible and insoluble in acids.

Kyanite (Disthene)

Al_2SiO_5 Triclinic **Habit** Crystals usually flat and bladed, seldom terminated; also as radiating, bladed aggregates. Crystals are distinctly flexible and often bent or twisted. **Colour** Commonly blue to white but may be grey or green, often a patchy blue; transparent to translucent. Vitreous lustre, sometimes pearly on cleavage surfaces. White streak. **Occurrence** Typically found in medium to high-grade regionally metamorphosed schists and gneisses; associated with garnet, staurolite, mica and quartz. Also occurs in some pegmatites and quartz veins associated with schists and gneisses. **Distinguishing properties** Habit; colour; S.G. $3 \cdot 5$–$3 \cdot 7$; hardness variable, $5\frac{1}{2}$ along the length of the crystals and 6–7 across; one perfect and one good cleavage; also a basal parting.

Staurolite

$(Fe,Mg)_2(Al,Fe)_9Si_4O_{22}(O,OH)_2$
Monoclinic (pseudo-orthorhombic)
Habit Usually as prismatic crystals, often with rough surfaces; rarely massive. Twinning is common, as cruciform twins, forming crosses near 90° and also oblique crosses at about 60°. **Colour** Reddish-brown to brown-black; translucent to nearly opaque. Vitreous to resinous lustre. Grey streak. **Occurrence** Typically found as porphyroblasts in medium-grade aluminium-rich schists and gneisses, often in association with garnet, kyanite and mica. **Distinguishing properties** Habit, (particularly if twinned); colour; S.G. 3·7–3·8; hardness 7–7½; distinct cleavage; uneven to subconchoidal fracture.

Ilvaite (illustrated)

$CaFe^{2+}_2Fe^{3+}Si_2O_8(OH)$ Orthorhom
Habit Crystals prismatic, of diamond-shaped in cross-secti
striated along the length; also colum
or massive. **Colour** Black; opaq
Dull submetallic lustre. Black stre
Occurrence Found chiefly as a cont
metasomatic mineral, in iron-, zir
and copper-ore deposits. **Distinguis
ing properties** Habit and streak; S
3·8–4·1; hardness 5½–6; distinct ba
cleavage; uneven fracture.

Bertrandite

$H_2Be_4Si_2O_9$ Orthorhombic **Ha
Small tabular or prismatic cryst
Heart-shaped twins. **Colour** Colo
less to pale yellow. **Occurrence** Fou
in pegmatites associated with ber
Distinguishing properties Habit; a
sociation; S.G. 2·6; hardness 6-
prismatic cleavage.

paz

$SiO_4(OH,F)_2$ Orthorhombic **Habit**
well-developed short to long pris-
tic crystals, sometimes striated;
en with well-developed termin-
ons; also massive, granular. **Colour**
lourless or white, pale blue and
low, yellow-brown, rarely pink;
nsparent to translucent. Vitreous
tre. White streak. **Occurrence**
pically found in granite pegmatites,
jh-temperature quartz veins, and
olites. As grains in granites which
ve been altered by fluorine-rich
lutions and characteristically associ-
ed with fluorite, tourmaline, apatite,
ryl and cassiterite. Also as rounded
ains or pebbles in alluvial deposits.
stinguishing properties Habit; S.G.
5–3·6; hardness 8; perfect basal
eavage; subconchoidal to uneven
cture.

Euclase (illustrated)

$BeAlSiO_4(OH)$ Monoclinic **Habit**
Usually found as prismatic crystals.
Colour Colourless to pale blue-green;
transparent to translucent. Vitreous
lustre. **Occurrence** A rare mineral
found in pegmatites in association
with beryl. **Distinguishing properties**
Habit; colour; association; S.G. 3·0–
3·1; hardness $7\frac{1}{2}$; one perfect cleavage.

Gadolinite

$Be_2Fe(YO)_2(SiO_4)_2$ Monoclinic. Other
rare earth elements substitute for
yttrium. **Habit** Prismatic crystals but
usually massive. **Colour** Black, sometimes brown; vitreous lustre. **Occurrence** In pegmatite veins, frequently
associated with allanite. **Distinguishing properties** Colour; habit and
association; S.G. 4–4·5; hardness
6·5–7.

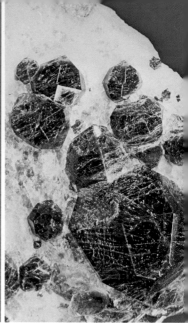

Sphene (Titanite)

$CaTiSiO_5$ Monoclinic **Habit** Crystals commonly flattened and wedge-shaped, also massive. Twinning is common, forming contact or cruciform penetration twins. **Colour** Brown and yellowish-green common, green to grey; transparent to nearly opaque. Resinous to adamantine lustre. White streak. **Occurrence** Widely distributed as an accessory mineral in intermediate and acid igneous rocks and associated pegmatites. Also in schists, gneisses and some metamorphosed limestones. Rarely as a detrital mineral in sediments. **Distinguishing properties** S.G. 3·4–3·6; hardness 5–5½; prismatic distinct cleavage; conchoidal fracture. Sharp, wedge-shaped habit, adamantine lustre and colour are particularly distinctive.

Garnet Group

Cubic. The garnets comprise a grou isomorphous minerals with the gen formula $X_3Y_2Si_3O_{12}$ in which X may Ca, Mn, Mg or Fe^{2+} and Y may Al, Cr or Fe^{3+}. The following nar are in common use: almano $Fe_3Al_2Si_3O_{12}$); pyrope (Mg$_3$ Si_3O_{12}); spessartine (Mn$_3$Al$_2$Si$_3$O grossular (Ca$_3$Al$_2$Si$_3$O$_{12}$); andrac (Ca$_3$Fe$_2$Si$_3$O$_{12}$); uvarovite (Ca$_3$ Si_3O_{12}). Considerable atomic st stitution may occur between the **Habit** Crystals are common, usua rhombdodecahedral or icositetrahed Sometimes massive or granular. **Col** Pyrope, almandine and spessartine usually shades of deep-red and bro to nearly black; grossular is brown, p green or white; andradite is yello brown or black; uvarovite is gre Transparent to translucent. Vitreous resinous lustre. Normally white stre **Occurrence** Pyrope occurs in ult basic igneous rocks such as peridot and high-grade, magnesium-r metamorphic rocks. Almandine is

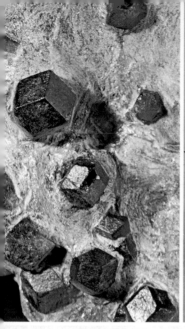

mon garnet of schists and gneisses.
ssartine occurs in low-grade meta-
phic rocks. Uvarovite occurs in
ociation with chromite in
entinite. Grossular is formed by the
tact or regional metamorphism of
ure limestones. Andradite is comnly formed by the metasomatic
ration of limestones by iron-bearing
itions. The black variety, melanite
nium andradite), occurs in some
spathoidal igneous rocks. Also
nd as a constituent of beach and
r sands. **Distinguishing properties**
it; colour and mode of occurrence
n indicate the garnet species
sent; S.G. 3·6–4·3 (varies with
position); hardness $6\frac{1}{2}$–$7\frac{1}{2}$; sub-
choidal fracture. Chemical analysis
mally required for precise com-
ition. Some varieties cut as gem-
es, mainly pyrope (red-brown).

Idocrase (Vesuvianite)

$Ca_{10}(Mg,Fe)_2Al_4(SiO_4)_5(Si_2O_7)_2(OH,F)_4$
Tetragonal **Habit** Mainly as short
prismatic crystals, often with striations
parallel to their length; also massive,
granular or columnar. **Colour** Various
shades of green, dark green, brown,
white-yellow; blue varieties are called
cyprine; transparent to translucent.
Vitreous to resinous lustre. White
streak. **Occurrence** Formed by the
contact metamorphism of impure limestones; commonly associated with
calcite, grossularite or andradite garnet
and wollastonite. Often in blocks of
limestone erupted from Mount
Vesuvius. **Distinguishing properties**
Prismatic, striated crystal form; S.G.
3·3–3·5; hardness 6–7; poor prismatic
cleavage; uneven to conchoidal
fracture.

Hemimorphite (Calamine)

$Zn_4Si_2O_7(OH)_2.H_2O$ Orthorhombic
Habit Crystals are tabular; also massive, fibrous or mamillated. **Colour** White, sometimes blue, greenish or brownish; transparent to translucent. Vitreous lustre. White streak. **Occurrence** A secondary mineral found in the oxidized zone of zinc-bearing ore bodies usually very close to the surface; also in limestones. Associated with galena, sphalerite, smithsonite, cerussite and anglesite. **Distinguishing properties** Crystal form; S.G. 3·4–3·5; hardness $4\frac{1}{2}$–5; perfect prismatic cleavage; conchoidal to uneven fracture. Soluble in hydrochloric acid but without effervescence. The name calamine is also often applied to smithsonite.

Epidote Group

The general formula is $X_2Y_3Si_3O_{12}($ (in which X is commonly Ca, p replaced by rare earth elements allanite, and Y is Al and Fe^{3+} p replaced by Mg and Fe^{2+} in allar and by Mn^{3+} in piemontite.

Zoisite

$Ca_2Al_3Si_3O_{12}(OH)$ Orthorhon
Habit As aggregates of long prism crystals, often deeply striated c monly massive. **Colour** White, g greenish-brown, green, also (thulite), blue to purple (tanzan transparent to translucent. Vitre lustre, pearly on cleavage surfa White to grey-white streak. **Occ rence** Found in schists and gneis and in metasomatic rocks, toge with garnet, idocrase and actino Occasionally formed in hydrother veins. **Distinguishing proper** Colour; S.G. 3·2–3·4; hardness perfect pinacoidal cleavage; une fracture.

nozoisite and
dote (illustrated)

$Al_3Si_3O_{12}(OH)$ and
$(Al,Fe)_3Si_3O_{12}(OH)$ Monoclinic
)it   Crystals are prismatic, often
ply striated parallel to their length;
stly massive, granular or fibrous.
inning is lamellar, but not common.
our   Pale green, or greenish-grey
nozoisite); yellowish-green to black
idote); transparent to nearly
.que. Vitreous lustre. White, grey-
te streak. **Occurrence** Common in
'-medium grade metamorphic rocks.
) from calcareous sediments. Found
eins in igneous rocks. **Distinguish-
properties**   Habit; colour; S.G.
–3·5; hardness 6–7; one perfect
avage, usually parallel to the length
he crystals; uneven fracture.

Allanite (Orthite)

$(Ca,Ce,Y,La,Th)_2(Al,Fe)_3Si_3O_{12}(OH)$
Monoclinic. Commonly metamict, as a
result of radiation damage caused by
radioactive decay of thorium.   **Habit**
Crystals usually tabular, long prismatic
to acicular;   commonly compact
massive.   **Colour**   Usually black,
sometimes light to dark brown.
Vitreous lustre, sometimes pitchy.
Grey-brown   streak.   **Occurrence**
Found as a widespread accessory
mineral in many granites, and pegmatites, syenites, gneisses and skarns.
Distinguishing properties   Colour and
lustre; S.G. 3·4–4·2 (variable); hardness 5–6½; two poor cleavages; conchoidal to uneven fracture. Often
weakly radioactive, the rock matrix
around the crystals is often stained
black as a result.

Piemontite (Piedmontite)

$Ca_2(Al,Fe,Mn)_3Si_3O_{12}(OH)$ Monoclinic **Habit** Crystals usually prismatic or acicular; commonly massive. Twinning is lamellar, but not common. **Colour** Red, reddish-brown to reddish-black; transparent to nearly opaque. Vitreous lustre. **Occurrence** A rare mineral, found in some low-grade schists, and also in metasomatic manganese-ore deposits. **Distinguishing properties** Colour; occurrence; S.G. 3·4–3·5; hardness 6; one perfect cleavage; uneven fracture.

Wollastonite

$CaSiO_3$ Triclinic **Habit** Crys tabular or short prismatic; usu. fibrous masses, sometimes granu and compact. Twinning is comm **Colour** White to grey; transparent translucent. Vitreous lustre, somew silky in fibrous varieties. White stre **Occurrence** Formed by the me morphism of siliceous limestones, b in contact aureoles or in high-gra regionally metamorphosed roc usually associated with calcite, epid grossular and tremolite. **Distinguish properties** Habit; colour; associati S.G. 2.8–3·1; hardness $4\frac{1}{2}$–5; c perfect, two other good cleavag splintery fracture. Dissolves in hyd chloric acid with separation of silic

ctolite

Ca$_2$Si$_3$O$_8$OH Triclinic **Habit** As
gregates of fibrous or acicular crys-
;; usually radiating and forming
bular masses. **Colour** Colourless,
ite; transparent to translucent. Vit-
us or silky lustre. White streak.
currence Chiefly found in cavities
basaltic rocks, often in association
h zeolites; less commonly in cal-
m-rich metamorphic rocks, also in
ne alkaline igneous rocks. **Disguishing properties** The globular
gregates and radiating structures on
cture surfaces are characteristic;
3. 2·8–2·9; hardness $4\frac{1}{2}$–5; two
fect cleavages; splintery fracture.
sily fusible. Decomposed by hydro-
oric acid.

Benitoite

BaTiSi$_3$O$_9$ Hexagonal **Habit** Crystals
are rare, pyramidal or tubular, somewhat triangular in shape. **Colour** Blue,
purple, pink or white; transparent to
translucent. Vitreous lustre. White
streak. **Occurrence** As superb blue
crystals in association with neptunite
and natrolite on serpentine from localities in San Benito County
California, United States. Also rarely
occurs as detrital grains. **Distinguishing properties** Triangular habit; colour
and association with white natrolite
and black neptunite are characteristic.
S.G. 3·6; hardness $6–6\frac{1}{2}$; indistinct
cleavage; conchoidal to uneven
fracture. Fluoresces under short-wave
ultraviolet light.

Beryl

$Be_3Al_2Si_6O_{18}$ Hexagonal **Habit**
Crystals are usually short to long
prismatic, faces often striated parallel to
their length and etched. **Colour**
Commonly pale green, white or yellow;
translucent. Gem varieties are transparent, light to dark green (emerald),
pale blue or green (aquamarine),
yellow (heliodor), pink (morganite).
Vitreous lustre. White streak. **Occurrence** Chiefly as an accessory mineral
in granite and granite-pegmatites in
which crystals often grow to a very
large size. Also found in some biotite
schists, gneisses and pneumatolytic
hydrothermal veins. **Distinguishing
properties** Hexagonal crystal form;
colour; S.G. 2·6–2·8 (used to distinguish from quartz when massive
white beryl); hardness $7\frac{1}{2}$–8 (compare
apatite) poor basal cleavage; conchoidal to uneven fracture.

Cordierite

$(Mg,Fe)_2Al_4Si_5O_{18}$. Orthorhom
Habit Rarely as prismatic or pseu
hexagonal twinned crystals; gener
massive or irregular grains. Twinnin
common, usually repeated form
pseudohexagonal crystals. **Col**
Dark blue-violet, greyish-blue, a
colourless, yellow, grey or brov
transparent to translucent. Vitre
lustre. White streak. **Occurre**
Formed by medium- to high-gr
metamorphism of aluminium-r
rocks. Commonly found in hornf
schists and gneisses. **Distinguish
properties** Colour; granular, colourl
or grey cordierite resembles quartz a
has to be identified by optical
chemical tests. The gem variety (ioli
is recognized by its intense pleochroi
(deep blue to yellow); S.G. 2·5–
(increasing with iron content); ha
ness 7–$7\frac{1}{2}$; one poor cleavage; su
conchoidal fracture.

...optase

$SiO_2(OH)_2$ Hexagonal (Trigonal)
...bit Crystals short to long prismatic,
...en terminated by rhombohedra; also
...ssive. **Colour** Emerald-green;
...nsparent to translucent. Vitreous
...tre. Pale greenish-blue streak.
...currence Not common but oc-
...sionally found in the oxidized zone
... copper deposits, sometimes as
...ll-developed crystals associated
...th other copper minerals and calcite.
...stinguishing properties The colour
... dioptase distinguishes it from other
...nerals found in copper deposits.
...3·3; hardness 5; perfect rhombo-
...dral cleavage; conchoidal to uneven
...cture.

Pyroxene Group

The pyroxenes are a widely distributed
group of rock-forming silicates. They
have a general formula $X_2Si_2O_6$ and
are characterized by two cleavages
which intersect almost at right angles.

Orthopyroxenes

Enstatitie and Hypersthene

$MgSiO_3$ and $(Mg,Fe)SiO_3$ Orthorhombic **Habit** Crystals prismatic;
usually as grains or massive. **Colour**
Pale green to dark brownish-green-
black (darkening with Fe). Bronzite is
intermediate between enstatite and
hypersthene, having a bronzy lustre;
translucent to nearly opaque. Vitreous
or pearly lustre. White to grey streak.
Occurrence Found in basic and
ultrabasic rocks poor in calcium such
as pyroxenites, peridotites and norites.
Also in some high-grade metamorphic
rocks. **Distinguishing properties**
Colour; S.G. 3·4—4·0; (increasing with
Fe); hardness 5—6; good prismatic
cleavage; uneven fracture.

Clinopyroxenes

Diopside-Hedenbergite-Augite Series

$Ca(Mg,Fe)Si_2O_6$: $Ca(Mg,Fe,Al)$ $(Al,Si)_2O_6$ Monoclinic. These minerals form a continuous series, of which augite is the most common. **Habit** Crystals are usually stout prisms of square or octagonal cross-section; also massive, granular. Twinning is common. **Colour** Dark green to black (augite); greyish white to light green (diopside); translucent to opaque, rarely transparent. Vitreous lustre. White or grey streak. **Occurrence** Augite is abundant in basic and ultrabasic rocks, characteristic of gabbros and basalts. Diopside and hedenbergite occur in medium- and high-grade metamorphic rocks especially those rich in calcium. Light green diopside occurs commonly in metamorphosed dolomite limestones. **Distinguishing properties** Habit; S.G. 3·2–3·6 (increasing with Fe); hardness $5\frac{1}{2}$–$6\frac{1}{2}$; good prismatic cleavage, sometimes well developed basal parting.

Jadeite

$NaAlSi_2O_6$ Monoclinic **Habit** Crys are very rare; normally found as f granular or dense masses. **Col** Various shades of light or dark gre sometimes white or lilac; transluce Vitreous lustre, perhaps pearly. Wh streak. **Occurrence** Formed at h pressures and occurs in metam phosed sodic sediments and volca rocks often associated with amphibole-glaucophane group. Fou also as discrete grains. Twinning sociated with serpentine. **Distinguis ing properties** Habit; colour; S 3·2–3·4; hardness 6–$6\frac{1}{2}$; good pr matic cleavage; fine grained mass material extremely tough; splint fracture. The name 'jade' used for semi-precious stone is applied to t distinct minerals, jadeite and nephr (an amphibole).

girine

FeSi$_2$O$_6$. Monoclinic A solid
ution series exists between aegirine
d augite. **Habit** Usually as slender
smatic crystals, often elongated and
minated by steeply inclined faces
ing a pointed appearance (acmite);
o as discrete grains. Twinning is
mmon. **Colour** Usually dark green
black; subtransparent to opaque.
reous lustre. Grey streak. **Occur-
ce** Found in sodium-rich igneous
ks, especially in nepheline syenites
d associated pegmatites. **Disguishing properties** Habit; associ-
on; S.G. 3·5–3·6; hardness 6; good
smatic cleavage; uneven fracture.

Spodumene

LiAlSi$_2$O$_6$ Monoclinic **Habit** Crystals
usually prismatic or lath-like, often
striated along their length also massive
and columnar, etched and corroded.
Twinning is common. **Colour** Commonly white or grey; some varieties are
transparent, pink-violet (kunzite) or
green (hiddenite) resulting from the
presence of small quantities of chromium; translucent. Vitreous lustre.
White streak. **Occurrence** Found
typically in lithium-bearing granite
pegmatites associated with lepidolite,
tourmaline and beryl. **Distinguishing
properties** Habit; occurrence and
association; S.G. 3·0–3·2; hardness
6½–7; perfect prismatic cleavage, usually with a well-developed parting;
uneven splintery fracture. Colours a
flame red (lithium). Alters readily to
clay minerals.

Amphibole Group

Widely distributed in igneous and metamorphic rocks. The amphibole minerals are characterized by two cleavages intersecting at about 120°. The amphiboles contain essential hydroxyl groups in their structure.

Anthophyllite

$(Mg,Fe)_7Si_8O_{22}(OH)_2$ Orthorhombic **Habit** Individual crystals rare, usually in aggregates of prismatic crystals; sometimes fibrous and asbestiform. **Colour** White, grey or brown; translucent. Vitreous lustre, somewhat silky in fibrous varieties. White streak. **Occurrence** Typically found in medium-grade magnesium-rich metamorphic rocks, often associated with talc or cordierite. **Distinguishing properties** Habit; colour; S.G. 2·9–3·3 (increasing with Fe content); hardness 6; perfect prismatic cleavage.

Cummingtonite

$(Fe,Mg)_7Si_8O_{22}(OH)_2$ Monocli. Iron rich varieties of cummingtonite called grunerite; manganese is son times present replacing part of the i and magnesium. **Habit** Usually aggregates of fibrous crystals; of radiating. **Colour** Pale to dark bro. Vitreous lustre, fibrous variety, si White streak. **Occurrence** Found calcium-poor, iron-rich mediu grade metamorphic rocks, often association with ore deposits. Also some igneous rocks such as rhyoli and as a replacement product pyroxenes in diorites. **Distinguish properties** Colour; S.G. 3·2–3·6 (creasing with Fe content); hardness prismatic, perfect cleavage.

emolite-Actinolite

$_2(Mg,Fe)_5Si_8O_{22}(OH)_2$ Monoclinic.
emolite is the low-iron end of a
npositional series and actinolite is
 iron-rich member. **Habit** Normally
aggregates of long prismatic crystals;
metimes massive, fibrous. **Colour**
ite to grey (tremolite) becoming
een with increasing iron content.
reous lustre. White streak. **Occur-
nce** Common in low- and medium-
ade metamorphic rocks, tremolite
ing characteristic of thermally meta-
orphosed dolomite limestones;
tinolite generally occurs in schists
med by low-medium grade meta-
orphism of basic igneous rocks.
stinguishing properties Habit;
lour; S.G. 2·9–3·4; hardness 5–6;
od prismatic cleavage. Does not
ict with hydrochloric acid.

Glaucophane-Riebeckite Series

$Na_2(Mg,Fe,Al)_5Si_8O_{22}(OH)_2$ Monoclinic **Habit** Well-developed crystals
rare; often prismatic or acicular,
sometimes fibrous or asbestiform.
Colour Glaucophane is grey, grey-
blue or lavender-blue, riebeckite is
dark blue to black; translucent to
subtranslucent. Vitreous lustre, silky in
fibrous varieties. White to blue-grey
streak. **Occurrence** Glaucophane is
typically found in sodium-rich schists
formed by the low-temperature, high-
pressure metamorphism of synclinal
sediments, usually associated with
jadeite, aragonite, chlorite and garnet.
Riebeckite occurs mainly in alkaline
igneous rocks such as some granites, or
nepheline syenites. Fibrous riebeckite
(crocidolite or blue asbestos) occurs
in veins in bedded ironstones. **Distinguishing properties** Habit; colour
and association; S.G. 3·0–3·4 (increasing with Fe content); hardness 5–6;
good prismatic cleavage; uneven
fracture.

Hornblende

$(Ca,Na)_{2-3}(Mg,Fe,Al)_5(Si,Al)_8O_{22}(OH)_2$
Monoclinic. Varieties occurring in basic igneous rocks often contain appreciable amounts of titanium (kaersutite), or may be low in hydroxyl (basaltic hornblende). **Habit** Crystals usually short or long prismatic, often with six-sided cross sections; also massive, granular or fibrous. Twinning is common. **Colour** Light green to dark green, nearly black; translucent to nearly opaque. Vitreous lustre. White to grey streak. **Occurrence** Very common rock-forming mineral. A common constituent of granodiorites, diorites, gabbros and their fine-grained equivalents. Also in medium-grade, regionally metamorphosed rocks such as amphibolites and hornblende schists. **Distinguishing properties** Colour; S.G. 3·0–3·5 (increasing with Fe content); hardness 5–6; good prismatic cleavage; uneven fracture.

Rhodonite

$MnSiO_3$ Triclinic **Habit** Crystals common, but prismatic or tabu most commonly massive or granu **Colour** Pink to rose-red, often vein by black manganese alteration p ducts; transparent to translucent. V reous lustre. White streak. **Occurren** Commonly found associated with ma ganese-ore deposits either as hyd thermal or metasomatic veins; occ in some metamorphosed manganes bearing sediments. **Distinguishi properties** Colour; S.G. 3·5–3 hardness $5\frac{1}{2}$–$6\frac{1}{2}$; two perfect a good basal cleavages, conchoidal uneven fracture. Does not efferves with warm hydrochloric acid.

ica Group

e micas constitute an isomorphous up with a general formula of $(X,Y)_{2-3}Z_4O_{10}(OH,F)_2$. In this W is nerally potassium, X and Y can be minium, magnesium, iron and ium, and Z is silicon and aluminium.

uscovite

$l_2(AlSi_3O_{10})(OH)_2$ Monoclinic bit Crystals tabular and hexagonal outline; usually as lamellar masses small flakes. **Colour** Colourless, or le shades of green, grey or brown; nsparent to translucent. Vitreous tre; pearly parallel to cleavage. ite streak. **Occurrence** Very mmon in alkali granites and peg- atites. Also common in schists and eisses of low-medium grade meta- orphism. Often found as flakes in ndstones and siltstones. **Dis- guishing properties** Habit; S.G. 3–2·9; Hardness $2\frac{1}{2}$–4; perfect basal eavage; cleavage flakes are flexible d elastic.

Biotite and Phlogopite

$K(Mg,Fe)_3AlSi_3O_{10}(OH)_2$ and $K.Mg_3AlSi_3O_{10}(OH)_2$ Monoclinic **Habit** Crystals tabular or short pseudo-hexagonal prisms; also as lamellar aggregates or disseminated flakes. **Colour** Phlogopite, pale yellow to brown, often with a distinctive coppery appearance; biotite, black, dark brown or greenish-black; transparent to trans-lucent. Vitreous lustre, pearly on cleav-age surfaces. White or grey streak. **Occurrence** Phlogopite is most com-monly found in metamorphosed lime-stones and in magnesium-rich igneous rocks. Biotite is widely distributed in granite, diorite and syenite, and mica lamprophyres. Commonly found in metamorphic schists and gneisses. **Distinguishing properties** Colour; S.G. 2·7–3·4 (increasing with iron content); hardness 2–3; perfect basal cleavage.

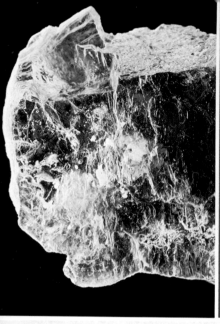

Lepidolite

$K(Li,Al)_3(Si,Al)_4O_{10}(OH)_2$ Monoclinic **Habit** Crystals tabular, pseudo-hexagonal; usually as small dis-seminated flakes. **Colour** Commonly pale lilac, also colourless, pale yellow or grey; transparent to translucent. Vitreous lustre, pearly on cleavage surfaces. **Occurrence** Found in granite pegmatites, often in association with lithium-bearing tourmaline and spodumene. The mineral is mined as a source of lithium compounds. **Distinguishing properties** Habit and colour; S.G. 2·8–3·3; hardness $2\frac{1}{2}$–3; perfect basal cleavage, giving flexible and elastic flakes.

Vermiculite (illustrated)

$Mg_3(Al,Si)_4O_{10}(OH)_2.4H_2O$ Mor clinic **Habit** As platy crystals. **Col** Yellow, brown; translucent. Pe lustre, often bronzy. White stre **Occurrence** Found as an alterat product of magnesium micas, of in association with carbonatites. **D** tinguishing properties Habit a colour; S.G. about 2·3; hardness abe $1\frac{1}{2}$. On heating, vermiculite expar greatly perpendicular to cleavage.

Illite

Monoclinic. An aluminosilicate potassium structurally related to t micas. **Habit** Massive and fir grained. **Colour** White or other p colour. **Occurrence** A clay mine present in shales and sediments. Al as a hydrothermal mineral. **D** tinguishing properties S.G. 2·6–2 hardness 1–2; association.

auconite (illustrated)

Fe,Mg,Al)$_2$(Si$_4$O$_{10}$)(OH)$_2$ Mono-
ic **Habit** As small, rounded
gregates. **Colour** Green to black,
en weathers brown. Earthy and
ll lustre. Green streak. **Occurrence**
rmed usually in marine sedimentary
:ks. The related mineral species,
adonite, is similar in structure and
mposition to glauconite, but is
med as a blue-green earthy material
vesicular cavities in basalts. **Disguishing properties** Habit and
lour; S.G. 2·5–2·8; hardness 2;
rfect basal cleavage.

piolite
g$_2$(Si$_3$O$_6$)(OH)$_4$ Monoclinic **Habit**
mpact mineral with soft, earthy
xture. **Colour** White or other pale
ades; opaque. **Occurrence** A
condary mineral often associated
th serpentine. **Distinguishing**
operties S.G. 2; hardness 2–2½.

Talc (Steatite, Soapstone)

Mg$_3$Si$_4$O$_{10}$(OH)$_2$ Monoclinic **Habit**
Crystals are rare; usually as granular
or foliated masses. **Colour** White, grey
or pale green, often stained reddish;
translucent. Dull lustre, pearly on
cleavage surfaces White to pale-green
streak. **Occurrence** Found as a
secondary mineral formed as a result of
the alteration of olivine, pyroxene and
amphibole, often lining faults in basic
rocks. Also found in low-medium
grade metamorphic rocks formed from
magnesium-rich rocks, often associated with actinolite. Sometimes formed
as a result of the thermal metamorphism of dolomite limestones. **Distinguishing properties** Habit; colour;
S.G. 2·6–2·8; hardness 1 (extreme
softness); soapy feel; perfect basal
cleavage.

Chlorite Group

$(Mg, Fe, Al)_6 (Al, Si)_4 O_{10} (OH)_8$ Monoclinic **Habit** Crystals are tabular often pseudohexagonal, rarely prismatic; also as scaly aggregates, and massive, earthy. **Colour** Usually green; manganese varieties are orange-brown; chromium-bearing varieties, violet. Vitreous to earthy lustre. White, pale-green streak. **Occurrence** Often found in igneous rocks as an alteration product of pyroxenes, amphiboles and micas. In lavas, infilling amygdales. It is a characteristic mineral of low-grade metamorphic rocks, and is present in the clay mineral fraction of many sediments. Chamosite is an iron-rich chlorite important as a constituent of some sedimentary iron ores. **Distinguishing properties** Habit; colour; S.G. 2·6–3·3 (increasing with Fe content); hardness 2–3; perfect basal cleavage, flakes flexible but not elastic.

Kaolinite

$Al_2 Si_2 O_5 (OH)_4$ Triclinic **Habit** microscopic pseudohexagonal p crystals; usually in earthy aggrega **Colour** White, sometimes stai brown or grey. Dull lustre, crystal plates pearly. White streak. **Occurre** A secondary mineral produced by alteration of aluminous silicates pecially the alkali feldspars. **D tinguishing properties** S.G. 2·6–2 hardness 2–2½; perfect basal cleava plastic feel. For positive identificat from other clay minerals, chemical a optical tests must be made. Dick nacrite and halloysite are mine similar in composition to kaolin X-ray is usually required for posit identification.

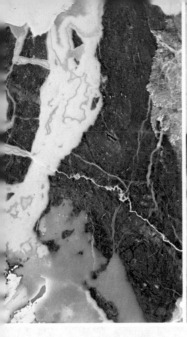

...rpentine Group

...$_3$Si$_2$O$_5$(OH)$_4$ Monoclinic. Serpen-
..., applies to material containing
... or more of the minerals chrysotile,
...igorite, and lizardite. **Habit** Anti-
...ite generally has a lamellar or platy
...cture; crystals virtually unknown.
...rysotile is fibrous. **Colour** Various
...des of green, also brownish; trans-
...ent to opaque. Waxy or greasy
...tre in massive varieties, silky in
...ous material. White streak. **Occur-**
...ce Formed by the alteration of
...vine and enstatite under conditions
... low- to medium-grade metamor-
...sm. Found typically in serpentinites
...ich have formed from the alteration
... olivine-rich rocks. **Distinguishing**
...perties Habit (chrysotile); colour;
...tre; smooth rather greasy feel; S.G.
...5–2·6; hardness, variable 2½–4; per-
...ct basal cleavage (antigorite and
...ardite), none in fibrous chrysotile.

Apophyllite

KCa$_4$Si$_8$O$_{20}$(F,OH).8H$_2$O Tetragonal
Habit Well-developed crystals of
varied habit, usually as combinations
of prism, bipyramid and pinacoid.
Colour Colourless white or grey,
sometimes pink to yellow; transparent
to translucent. Pearly lustre parallel to
basal cleavage, vitreous elsewhere.
White streak. **Occurrence** Occurs in
association with zeolites in cavities in
basalt, commonly associated with
prehnite, analcime, stilbite and calcite.
Found less commonly in cavities in
some granite, gneiss and limestones.
Also occurs in some hydrothermal
mineral veins. **Distinguishing proper-**
ties The basal pinacoid faces are often
rough and pitted. Lustre; S.G. 2·3–2·4;
hardness 4½–5; perfect ·basal, poor
prismatic cleavages; uneven fracture.

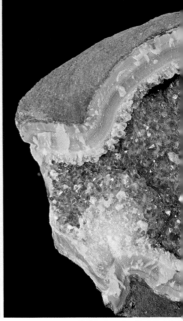

Silica Group

Includes those minerals whose composition is, SiO_2.

Quartz

SiO_2 Hexagonal (Trigonal) **Habit** Crystals are usually six-sided prisms, terminated by six faces, (two sets of rhombohedrons), prism faces may be striated at right angles to the length of the crystal. Shapes range from very elongated to equant. also massive. Most crystals are twinned, but this may be difficult to detect; the three common types are Dauphiné, the Brazil (penetration twins) and the Japan (contact twin). **Colour** Usually colourless (rock crystal) or white. Coloured varieties are often used as semi-precious stones: amethyst-purple; rose-quartz-pink; citrine-yellow brown; smoky quartz-brown to almost black; milky quartz-white. Some quartz varieties contain impurities – such as hair-like inclusions of rutile (rutilated quartz). Ferruginous quartz is a brick red or yellow. Opaque, 'tiger-eye',

compact is quartz that has repla fibrous asbestos fibres. Aventurine variety containing brilliant scales hematite or mica; transparent to tra lucent. Vitreous lustre. White str **Occurrence** Abundant, occurrin most igneous metamorphic and s mentary rocks, sometimes compos almost all of the rock, as in quartz (metamorphic) and some sandsto (sedimentary). Also as a gan mineral in mineral veins. Well-forr crystal groups are often obtained f geodes in granite pegmatites. Qu exists in two modifications depenc on the temperature of formation. **[tinguishing properties** Habit; S 2·65; hardness 7; conchoidal fract Usually fresh and unaltered. attacked by acids, other than hyc fluoric.

artz (variety Chalcedony)

Chalcedony is the name given to compact varieties of silica which are formed of quartz crystallites often fibrous in form and with sub-microscopic pores. **Habit** Massive, as mamillated, botryoidal or stalactitic forms. **Colour** Chalcedony is distinguished from agate by its lack of various colour banding, but exhibits the same range of colours: colourless, white, grey, red, brown, green or yellow. Some coloured varieties have various names: carnelian-red, sard-brown, chrysoprase-apple-green, heliotrope (bloodstone)-green with spots of red jasper; transparent to translucent. Jasper is opaque chalcedony and generally red but also yellow, brown and green varieties occur. Colour is often distributed in spots or bands. Vitreous to waxy lustre. **Occurrence** Found lining or filling cavities or fissures in rocks having been deposited from silica-rich aqueous solutions, usually formed at low to moderate temperatures by the crystallization of originally colloidal material. Chert and flint occur as dark nodules or thin beds in sedimentary rocks and originate either by the deposition of silica on the sea floor, or by the replacement of rocks, notably limestones, or by silica from percolating waters. **Distinguishing properties** Habit; colour; occurrence; S.G. about 2·6; hardness about $6\frac{1}{2}$; conchoidal fracture.

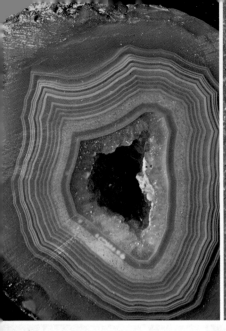
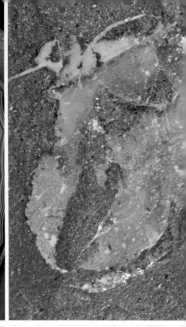

Quartz (variety Agate)

SiO_2 **Habit** Usually found as concentric or irregular layers lining a cavity, which may be partially or completely filled by quartz crystals. **Colour** The bands are usually variegated in shades of white, grey, green, brown, red or black. Commercial agate is often coloured artificially. Parallel banded agate in shades of white with black, brown or brownish red, is named onyx and sardonyx. Moss agate contains mineral impurities such as manganese oxides and chlorite in moss-like patterns. **Occurrence** Typically found in volcanic lavas as a cavity filling from silica-rich solutions. The colour banding may be due to slight changes in the composition of the solutions due to changing physical conditions. **Distinguishing properties** Habit; S.G. about 2·6; hardness about $6\frac{1}{2}$; conchoidal fracture.

Opal

$SiO_2.nH_2O$ Amorphous. Opal is hydrous submicrocrystalline form cristobalite. **Habit** Massive; veinlets, stalactitic or botryoidal. O replaces other substances such wood (wood opal). **Colour** Colourless, grey, red, brown and blue-gre Precious opal is milky-white, so times black, exhibiting a play of colour due to the internal structure; red yellow are dominant in fire o Common opal is translucent, lackin play of colours; transparent to tra lucent. Vitreous often resinous lus **Occurrence** Found filling and lir cavities in igneous and sedimen rocks, especially in areas of springs. Often forms skeletons organisms, e.g. sponges, accumula to form a fine-grained sedimen rock (diatomaceous earth). C tinguishing properties Lustre; S variable, 1·8–2·3; hardness $5\frac{1}{2}$– conchoidal fracture.

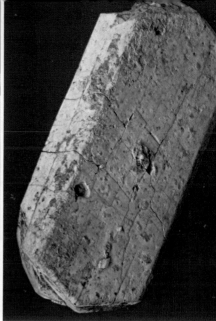

...dspar Group

...feldspars are the most abundant of ...minerals being widely distributed ...igneous, metamorphic and sedi-...tary rocks. The general formula is ...I,Si)$_4$O$_8$, X is Na,K,Ca or Ba.

...assic Feldspars

...crocline

...Si$_3$O$_8$ Triclinic **Habit** Usually ...rt prismatic. Simple twins, but ...ws repeated twinning. **Colour** ...ite, cream, pink; sometimes green ...azonstone); translucent to sub-...slucent. Vitreous lustre, sometimes ...rly on cleavage surfaces. White ...ak. **Occurrence** Usually forms ...ower temperatures than orthoclase ... is the common potassic feldspar ...egmatites and hydrothermal veins. ...o occurs in some metamorphic ...ks. **Distinguishing properties** From ...noclase only by optical properties. ...2·5–2·6; hardness 6; two good ...avages; conchoidal to uneven ...ture.

Orthoclase and Sanidine

KAlSi$_3$O$_8$ Monoclinic **Habit** Crystals usually prismatic; may be with square cross-section, sometimes flattened or tabular (sanidine). Twinning is common. **Colour** Sanidine is colourless to grey; transparent. Orthoclase is white to flesh-pink, occasionally red; translucent to subtranslucent. Vitreous lustre, sometimes pearly on cleavage surfaces. White streak. **Occurrence** Sanidine is the high-temperature form and it occurs as phenocrysts in volcanic rocks; also in metamorphic rocks. Orthoclase is the common potassic feldspar of most igneous and metamorphic rocks. Also occurs as perthitic intergrowth with albite. **Distinguishing features** Sanidine and orthoclase can be distinguished from the plagioclase feldspars by the absence of twinning striations. S.G. 2·5–2·6; hardness 6–6½; two perfect cleavages; conchoidal to uneven fracture.

113

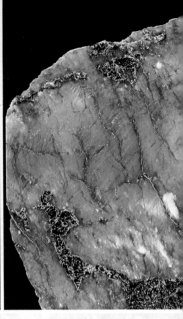

Adularia

KAlSi$_3$O$_8$ Monoclinic **Habit** Occurs as distinctive simple crystals, usually a combination of prisms terminated by two faces, which often have the appearance of rhombohedra. Twinning is common. **Colour** Colourless or milky white, often with a pearly sheen or play of colours (moonstones); transparent to translucent. Vitreous lustre. White streak. **Occurrence** Formed at low temperatures and is found in hydrothermal veins. **Distinguishing properties** Habit and occurrence; S.G. 2·6; hardness 6; two perfect cleavages; conchoidal to uneven fracture.

Plagioclase Feldspars

NaAlSi$_3$O$_8$CaAl$_2$Si$_2$O$_8$ Triclinic. composition changes progressi from albite (NaAlSi$_3$O$_8$) (illustra through oligoclase — andesine-la dorite-bytownite to anort (CaAl$_2$Si$_2$O$_8$). **Habit** Crystals p matic or tabular; also massive, granu .Repeated twinning is common albite and pericline laws and shows series of parallel striations, also sin twins, on Carlsbad, Baveno Manebach laws. **Colour** Usu white or off-white, sometimes p greenish or brownish; transparent translucent. Vitreous lustre, sometir pearly on cleavage surfaces. W streak. **Occurrence** The plagiocl feldspars occur in many igneous ro and are used as a basis of igneous r classification. In general the so plagioclases are found in gra igneous rocks and calcic plagiocla in basalts and gabbros. Between pot sic feldspar and albite there exist continuous series as sodium s stitutes for potassium; this series

ed the alkali feldspar series. Anor-
sites are rocks formed almost com-
ely of oligoclase-andesine plagio-
e feldspar. Albite is commonly
nd in pegmatites and in sodic lavas.
gioclase is also common in meta-
rphic rocks and as detrital grains.
tinguishing properties Repeated
n lamellae. Labradorite cleavages
nmonly show a play of colours in
des of blue and green (illustrated).
. 2·6–2·8; hardness 6–6½; two
d cleavages; uneven fracture.

Feldspathoid Group

Feldspathoid minerals are a group of
sodium and potassium aluminosilicates
which are formed in place of feldspars
when an alkali-rich magma is deficient
in silica.

Nepheline

$NaAlSiO_4$ Hexagonal **Habit** Crystals
are usually six-sided prisms, commonly
found as shapeless or irregular grains.
Colour Usually colourless, white or
grey but also brownish-red or greenish;
transparent to translucent. Vitreous to
greasy lustre. White streak. **Occurrence**
Characteristic mineral of silica-poor
alkali igneous rocks of both plutonic
and volcanic associations. **Distinguishing properties** Habit; lustre;
S.G. 2·6–2·7; hardness 5½–6; indistinct
prismatic and basal cleavages; conchoidal fracture. Readily decomposed
by hydrochloric acid.

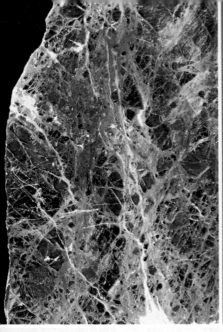
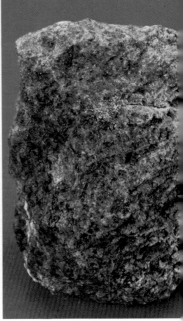

Sodalite

$Na_8Al_6Si_6O_{24}Cl_2$ Cubic **Habit** Crystals are rare, sometimes as small dodecahedral crystals; commonly massive and granular. **Colour** Commonly · azure-blue, also pink, yellow, green or grey-white; transparent to translucent. Vitreous lustre. White streak. **Occurrence** Often found associated with nepheline in alkali igneous rocks such as nepheline-syenites, also in some silica-poor dyke rocks and lavas. **Distinguishing properties** Colour; S.G. 2·3; hardness $5\frac{1}{2}$–6; poor dodecahedral cleavage; uneven to conchoidal fracture. Distinguished from lazurite by its occurrence and by the absence of associated pyrite. Often shows reddish flourescence in ultraviolet light. Gelatinizes in hydrochloric acid.

Hauyne (illustrated) and Nosean

$(Na,Ca)_{4-8}Al_6Si_6O_{24}(SO_4)_{1-2}$
$Na_8Al_6(SiO_4)_6SO_4$ Cubic H
Crystals usually dodecahedral or o hedral; commonly as rounded gra Twinning is common; sometimes penetration twins. **Colour** Often b also grey, brown, yellow-green; tra parent to translucent. Vitreous greasy lustre. White streak. **Occrence** Found in silica-poor lavas s as phonolites and related igne rocks in association with leucite nepheline. **Distinguishing proper** Colour, association; S.G. (hauy 2·4–2·5, (nosean) 2·3–2·4; hardr $5\frac{1}{2}$–6; poor dodecahedral cleav uneven to conchoidal fracture.

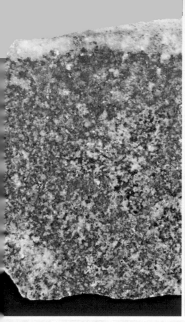

urite

,Ca)$_8$(Al,Si)$_{12}$O$_{24}$(S,SO$_4$) Cubic.
urite is isomorphous with sodalite
has sulphide ions in place of
ride ions. **Habit** Crystals rare;
ally as cubes or dodecahedra.
our Azure-blue; translucent. Vit-
us lustre. Bright-blue streak. **Occur-
ce** A rare mineral, usually occurring
rystalline limestones as a product of
tact metamorphism. Often in as-
iation with calcite and enclosing
all grains of pyrite. Lapis lazuli is a
k rich in lazurite and is used as a
orative stone. **Distinguishing
perties** Colour; association with
cite and pyrite; S.G. 2·4; hardness
$5\frac{1}{2}$; imperfect dodecahedral cleav-
. Soluble in hydrochloric acid.

Scapolite

(Na,Ca,K)$_4$Al$_3$(Al,Si)$_3$Si$_6$O$_{24}$(Cl,F,OH,
CO$_3$,SO$_4$) Tetragonal. Scapolites vary
between a sodic-end member
(marialite) and a calcic-end member
(meionite). **Habit** Crystals usually
prismatic, often with uneven faces;
mostly massive or granular. **Colour**
Usually white or grey, sometimes pink,
yellow or brownish; transparent to
translucent. Vitreous to pearly lustre.
White streak. **Occurrence** Found
typically in metamorphosed limestones,
occurs in skarns close to igneous
contacts, and in schists and gneisses
sometimes replacing plagioclase. **Distinguishing properties** Massive blocky
habit; colour; S.G. 2·5–2·8 (increasing
with calcium content); hardness 5–6;
good prismatic cleavages, these impart
a splintery appearance to massive
scapolite; subconchoidal fracture.

Leucite

$KAlSi_2O_6$ Tetragonal (pseudocubic). Leucite is tetragonal, pseudocubic at ordinary temperatures; cubic above 625°C. **Habit** Crystals nearly always icositetrahedra. **Colour** Usually white or grey; translucent. Vitreous lustre. White streak. **Occurrence** Found typically embedded in potassium-rich silica-poor lavas such as trachytes. Does not occur in plutonic igneous rocks. **Distinguishing properties** Crystal form and occurrence. Analcime also crystallizes as icositetrahedra but occurs typically in cavities, not as embedded crystals. S.G. 2·5; hardness $5\frac{1}{2}$–6; very poor cleavage; conchoidal fracture. Leucite often alters to pseudoleucite, a pseudomorph consisting of nepheline, analcime and orthoclase. Infusible.

Zeolite Group

Zeolites are hydrated alumino-silica chiefly of Na and Ca, less comme K, Ba, and Sr. They are not relate crystal structure but have a struc enclosing pores occupied by w molecules that can be continuo expelled on heating.

Analcime (Analcite)

$NaAlSi_2O_6 \cdot H_2O$ Cubic **Habit** Usu icositetrahedral; also granular and n sive. **Colour** Colourless, white or g often tinged with pink, yellow green; transparent to translucent. reous lustre. White streak. **Occurre** Commonly found as a second mineral in cavities, in basaltic rc associated with other zeolites. A in some sedimentary rocks as a seco ary mineral. Occasionally, as a prim mineral in silica-deficient igne rocks. **Distinguishing proper** Crystal form; mode of occurrer S.G. 2·2–2·3; hardness 5–$5\frac{1}{2}$; poor cubic cleavage; subconcho fracture.

abazite

$Al_2Si_4O_{12}.6H_2O$ Hexagonal (Trigal) **Habit** Usually occurs as simple mbohedral crystals which look like es. Penetration twins common. **our** Usually white, yellow, often kish or red; transparent to transent. Vitreous lustre. White streak. **currence** Typically occurs lining ities in basalts and andesites, asiated with other zeolites. **Disguishing properties** Crystal form; . 2·0–2·1; hardness 4–5; pour mbohedral cleavage; uneven frace. Does not effervesce in acid.

Natrolite

$Na_2Al_2Si_3O_{10}.2H_2O$ Orthorhombic (pseudotetragonal) **Habit** Usually as prismatic crystals, commonly elongated and needle-like; frequently as divergent or radiating aggregates. Also as compact masses. **Colour** Colourless to white, grey yellow or red; transparent to translucent. Vitreous lustre. White streak. **Occurrence** Typically occurs as crystals lining cavities in basaltic rocks. **Distinguishing properties** Habit; S.G. 2 2–2·3; hardness 5 $5\frac{1}{2}$; perfect prismatic cleavage. Mesolite and scolecite are also fibrous zeolites of similar composition and occurrence to natrolite, they are both monoclinic and fibrous; optical or X-ray tests are needed for positive identification.

Thomsonite

$NaCa_2(Al,Si)_{10}O_{20}.6H_2O$ Orthorhombic (pseudotetragonal) **Habit** Usually as acicular crystals in radiating or divergent aggregates. **Colour** White, sometimes tinged with red; transparent to translucent. Vitreous to pearly lustre. White streak. **Occurrence** Associated with other zeolites, in cavities in basalts and related igneous rocks. Also found as an alteration product of nepheline. **Distinguishing properties** Slightly more coarsely crystalline than natrolite. S.G. 2·1–2·4; hardness 5–5½; two good cleavages; uneven fracture.

Laumontite

$CaAl_2Si_4O_{12}.4H_2O$ Monoclinic Ha Commonly as small prismatic cryst often with oblique terminations; a massive, or as columnar and radiat aggregates. Frequently twinned, son times as 'swallow-tail' twins. **Col** White, sometimes reddish; transpar to translucent. Vitreous lustre, pea on cleavage surfaces. White stre **Occurrence** Occurs with other zeoli in veins and amygdales in igne rocks. It is also produced as a result very low-grade metamorphism of so sedimentary rocks and tuffs. **D tinguishing properties** Habit; S 2·2–2·4; hardness 3–4; two perf cleavages; uneven fracture. Charact istic alteration, laumonite loses part its water on exposure to dry air a becomes powdery, friable and cha (variety leonhardite).

..ulandite

..,Na$_2$)Al$_2$Si$_7$O$_{18}$.6H$_2$O . Monoclinic
..oit Crystals are usually tabular,
..ffin-shaped', often in subparallel
..gregates; also massive, granular.
..our Colourless, white, grey, pink,
.. or brown; transparent to trans-
..ent. Vitreous lustre, pearly on cleav-
.. surfaces. White streak. **Occurrence**
..ommon zeolite mineral, often assoc-
..ed with stilbite in cavities in basaltic
..ks, and sometimes found in sedi-
..ntary rocks as a secondary mineral.
..tinguishing properties Habit; lustre;
..   2·1–2·2; hardness 3½–4; one
..fect cleavage; uneven fracture.

Stilbite

NaCa$_2$Al$_5$Si$_{13}$O$_{36}$.14H$_2$O Monoclinic
Habit Commonly found as sheaf-like
aggregates formed by cruciform penetration twins; also massive or globular.
Twinning is common, forming cruciform interpenetrant twins. **Colour**
White sometimes yellowish or pink,
occasionally brick-red; transparent to
translucent. Vitreous lustre, pearly on
cleavage surfaces. White streak. **Occurrence** Found in cavities in basalts,
commonly in association with heu-
landite. **Distinguishing properties**
Habit; lustre; S.G. 2·1–2·2; hardness
3½–4; one perfect cleavage; uneven
fracture.

121

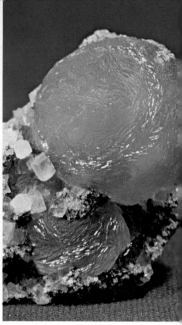

Petalite

$LiAlSi_4O_{10}$ Monoclinic **Habit** Crystals are well-formed but small; usually as large cleavable, blocky masses. Polysynthetic twinning. **Colour** Colourless, white, grey or yellow; transparent to translucent. Vitreous lustre, pearly on cleavages. White streak. **Occurrence** In granite pegmatites in association with cleavelandite, quartz and lepidolite. **Distinguishing properties** Association; S.G. 2·3–2·5; hardness 6–6½; two good cleavages; subconchoidal fracture.

Prehnite

$Ca_2Al_2Si_3O_{10}(OH)_2$ Orthorhom Habit Crystals rare, commonly tabu usually massive, botryoidal or sta titic. **Colour** Characteristically green, sometimes white, yellowish grey. Vitreous to somewhat pe lustre. White streak. **Occurre** Occurs chiefly in cavities in b igneous rocks, often associated zeolites; also in low-grade m morphic rocks and as an altera product in some altered igneous ro **Distinguishing properties** Ha colour; S.G. 2·9–3·0; hardness 6– good basal cleavage; uneven fract

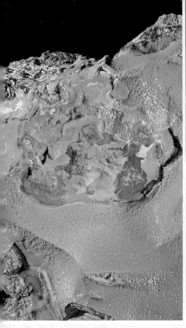

Chrysocolla

ar $CuSiO_3.2H_2O$ possibly Ortho-
rombic **Habit** Finely fibrous or
massive, sometimes botryoidal, earthy.
Colour Various shades of blue, blue-
green to green, sometimes brown to
black when impure; translucent to
nearly opaque. Vitreous, waxy, or
earthy lustre. White streak. **Occurrence**
A fairly common mineral in the oxidation zone of some copper deposits.
Distinguishing properties Habit;
colour; occurrence; S.G. variable, 2·0–
2·5; hardness 2–4; conchoidal to
uneven fracture.

Tourmaline

$Na(Mg,Fe)_3Al_6(BO_3)_3Si_6O_{18}(OH,F)_4$
Hexagonal (Trigonal). Tourmaline is a
general group term that is applied to
several minerals with similar atomic
structure and chemical composition.
The most common of these are elbaite
$Na(Li,Al)_3Al_6B_3Si_6O_{27}(OH,F)_4$; schorl
$Na(Fe,Mn)_3Al_6B_3Si_6O_{27}(OH,F)_4$; and
dravite $NaMg_3Al_6B_3Si_6O_{27}(OH,F)_4$.
Habit Crystals usually prismatic, often
with rounded triangular cross-sections;
prism faces commonly strongly striated parallel to their length; the two
ends of a crystal are often differently
terminated. Parallel or radiating crystal
groups are common. **Colour** Usually
black, especially schorl, also brown
dark blue, colourless (iron-free
varieties), pink, green and blue. Crystals are commonly colour-zoned;
transparent to nearly opaque. Names
of coloured varieties: rubellite (pink
and red); indicolite (blue); achroite
(colourless); siberite (reddish-violet).
Vitreous lustre. White streak. **Occurrence** Commonly in granitic peg-

123

Tourmaline (continued)

matites, or in granites which have
been metasomatically altered by boron-
rich fluids. Brown magnesium-rich
tourmaline is found in metamorphosed
limestone. Also found as an accessory
mineral in schists and gneisses. **Distinguishing properties** Habit; striations;
triangular cross-section; colour; S.G.
3.0–3.2; hardness 7–$7\frac{1}{2}$; very poor
cleavage; conchoidal to uneven
fracture.

Axinite

$(Ca, Mn, Fe, Mg)_3Al_2BSi_4O_{15}(OH)$
clinic **Habit** Crystals usually tab
and wedge-shaped with sharp edg
also massive, lamellar or granu
Colour Distinctive clove-brown colc
but sometimes yellow, grey or p
transparent to translucent. Vitre
lustre. White streak. **Occurrence** Cc
monly found in calcareous rocks t
have undergone contact metam
phism and metasomatism. Also occ
in cavities in granites and in so
hydrothermal veins. **Distinguish**
properties Crystal form; colour; S
3.3–3.4; hardness $6\frac{1}{2}$–7; one gc
cleavage; conchoidal fracture.

...tolite

...SiO_4OH Monoclinic   **Habit**
...ally in short prismatic crystals
...ch often show a variety of forms;
...s granular masses. **Colour** Colour-
... or pale shades of yellow and green,
... white; transparent. Vitreous lustre.
...te streak. **Occurrence** A secondary
...eral, usually found in cavities in
...ic igneous rocks associated with
...lites, prehnites and calcite. Also
...some veins and granites. **Dis-
...juishing properties.** Habit; colour;
...2·8–3·0; hardness 5–5½; uneven
...conchoidal fracture.

Dumortierite

$Al_7O_3(BO_3)(SiO_4)_3$ Orthorhombic
Habit   Rare as prismatic crystals,
usually in fibrous or columnar aggregates; frequently radiating.   **Colour**
Blue, violet or pink; transparent to
translucent. Vitreous or dull lustre.
White streak.   **Occurrence**   Not a
common mineral but occurs in considerable amounts at a few localities.
Found in some aluminium-rich metamorphic rocks and occasionally in
pegmatites. **Distinguishing properties**
Habit; colour: S.G. 3·3–3·4; hardness
8½; one good, one imperfect cleavage.

Further reading

The following publications are recommended for further reading on the study of rocks and minerals or as reference works.

Deer, W.A., Howie, R.A. and Zussman, J., *An introduction to the Rock Forming Minerals*, Longmans, London, 1966.

Ford, W.E., *Dana's Textbook of Mineralogy*, John Wiley, New York, 1932.

Greg, R.P. and Lettsom, W.G., *Mineralogy of Great Britain and Ireland*, 1858. Facsimile reprint, Lapidary Publications, Broadstairs, 1977.

Hamilton, W.R., Woolley, A.R. and Bishop, A.C., *The Hamlyn Guide to Minerals, Rocks and Fossils*, Hamlyn, London, 1974.

Hey, M.H., *Chemical Index of Minerals*, British Museum (Natural History), London, 1955, 1963, 1974.

Kostov, I., *Mineralogy*, Oliver and Boyd, Edinburgh and London, 1968.

Woolley, A.R. (ed.), *The Illustrated Encyclopedia of the Mineral Kingdom*, Hamlyn, London, 1978.

Index

Page numbers shown in italics refer to main descriptions.